DNA

Dᴇɴɴɪѕ Kᴇʟʟʏ

WORKBOOK

Notes and activities: Jane Branson
Series consultant: Peter Buckroyd

OXFORD
UNIVERSITY PRESS·

Contents

Introduction

What are Oxford Literature Companions?

Oxford Literature Companions is a series designed to provide you with comprehensive support for popular set texts. You can use the Companion workbook alongside your play, using relevant sections during your studies or using the workbook as a whole for revision. The workbook will help you to create your own personalised guide to the text.

What are the main features within this workbook?

Each workbook in the Oxford Literature Companion series follows the same approach and includes the following features:

Activities

Each workbook offers a range of varied and in-depth activities to deepen understanding and encourage close work with the text, covering characters, themes, language and context. The Skills and Practice chapter also offers advice on assessment and includes sample questions and student answers. There are spaces to write your answers throughout the workbook.

Key terms and quotations

Throughout the workbook, key terms are highlighted in the text and explained on the same page. There is also a detailed glossary at the end of the workbook that explains, in the context of the play, all the relevant literary terms highlighted.

Quotations from the play appear in blue text throughout this workbook.

Upgrade

As well as providing guidance on key areas of the play, throughout this workbook you will also find 'Upgrade' features. These are tips to help with your exam preparation and performance.

Progress check

Each chapter of the workbook ends with a 'Progress check'. Through self-assessment, these enable you to establish how confident you feel about what you have been learning and help you to set next steps and targets.

Which edition of the play has this workbook used?

Quotations have been taken from the Oberon Books edition of *DNA* (ISBN: 978-184002-952-9).

Plot and Structure

Understanding plot

Welcome to this workbook about *DNA* by Dennis Kelly. Here are a few initial tips to help make sure your reading of the play is enjoyable and productive.

- The first time you read the play, try to do it in one sitting. This should take one to two hours, and will give you a great sense of the whole story.

- After that, be prepared to read the play multiple times. This workbook will help by directing you to read different parts for different purposes.

- Remember that this is a play, written to be performed. While you are reading, imagine yourself as a member of the audience at a performance. Think about where the characters are onstage, how they interact with each other and how the **plot** is revealed through their **dialogue**.

- The play has a cast of 11 characters. Several scenes feature only two characters; other scenes feature a large group of speaking and non-speaking characters. Read the **stage directions** as carefully as the dialogue – use them to visualise what's going on.

- The setting of the play alternates between A Street, A Field and A Wood. Be aware of how Kelly indicates scene changes: each of the four main parts is divided into shorter scenes (with the breaks indicated by three asterisks).

> **cliffhanger** a tense and exciting ending to an episode that deliberately withholds the scene's resolution from the audience, leaving them wanting more
>
> **dialogue** speech between characters
>
> **plot** the main events of a play, novel, film or similar work, presented by the writer as an interrelated sequence
>
> **stage directions** indications from the playwright about how scenes should be presented or words should be spoken

Activity 1

Make a table to track your initial reactions to the play's key events. Here is an example showing the first two scenes, to get you started.

Scene/setting	My thoughts/possible audience reactions?
One, A Street	Confused at first! Two characters in the middle of a conversation. Dramatic first word – 'Dead?'. Lots of unfinished sentences. Street might be deserted? Characters might be whispering. Audience hooked by the mystery?
One, A Field 1	Leah talks A LOT and Phil is silent. She comes across as needy and in awe of him. Leah reveals some of her feelings and fears – 'Scared, Phil. I'm scared...' Phil just eats. Jan and Mark come in at the end – **cliffhanger**.
One, A Wood	
One, A Field 2	
Two, A Street	

Scene/setting	My thoughts/possible audience reactions?
Two, A Field 1	
Two, A Wood	
Two, A Field 2	
Three, A Street	
Three, A Field 1	
Three, A Wood	
Three, A Field 2	
Four, A Street	
Four, A Field	

Upgrade

Notice that this student is already thinking about the effect of the plot on the audience. You should do this too. You will never be asked simply to retell the story, so from an early stage always ask yourself: what effect might the plot, action or dialogue have on the audience?

Sequencing and summarising

Keeping track of the action is important: by the time you get to the exam, you will need to have strong recall of all the major scenes and events in the play.

Activity 2

Listed below are some of the main events in the play. Number the events 1 to 10, to show the sequence in which they are recounted in the play.

Phil eats a muffin

Leah compares humans to chimpanzees and bonobos

John Tate bans the word 'dead'

Leah shows Phil the remains of her dead pet

Phil offers Leah a sweet

Adam appears looking *'like a tramp'*

Richard tells Phil about a rumour that Cathy has **'cut a first year's finger off'**

Phil puts a plastic bag over Brian's head

Jan and Mark describe how everyone threw stones at Adam until he fell into **'the grille'**

Danny describes his plans to be a dentist

Activity 3

Make a record of the six scenes between Leah and Phil which take place in 'A Field' and write a few notes on each to help you to distinguish between them. For example, you might make a note of what Phil is eating and what Leah talks about.

One, A Field 1

One, A Field 2

Two, A Field 1

Two, A Field 2

Three, A Field 1

Three, A Field 2

Activity 4

List the four scenes between Jan and Mark that take place in 'A Street' and write a few notes on each to help you distinguish between them. For example, you might make a note of what key questions Jan asks or what information emerges for the audience.

One, A Street

Two, A Street

Three, A Street

Four, A Street

Activity 5

Reread the three large group scenes, which all take place in 'A Wood', and complete this table about them. Don't forget to include all the characters, even those who say very little.

Scene summary	Characters featured	One key quotation per character
One, A Wood		
Two, A Wood		
Three, A Wood		

Silent characters are just as important as speakers. If a character is onstage but not talking, think about what they are doing and what their silence might suggest to the audience.

> **Key quotation**
>
> *They say nothing. RICHARD steps forward, a little hesitantly.*
>
> RICHARD: You shouldn't threaten me, John.
>
> JOHN TATE: I beg your pardon.
>
> *(One, A Wood)*

Activity 6

Now work further on your ability to recall and summarise the whole plot. Think carefully about what you need to focus on and leave out. This will help you to reflect on the key episodes.

a) Write the entire plot in five bullet points.

_____

_____

_____

_____

_____

b) Summarise the play in four sentences.

_____

_____

_____

_____

_____

_____

Offstage action

In this play, some of the key actions happen **offstage** and are reported through dialogue. The parts of the plot that Kelly has decided *not* to show the audience are just as important as the parts we see first-hand. Offstage action can help to increase the tension and sense of drama for the audience because they find out about things at the same time as other characters. Having some events happen offstage might be linked to the writer's overall intentions, what characters the writer wants to focus on and what he wants the audience experience to be like. It could also be a practical decision, based on what is possible to enact or create in front of the audience.

offstage not on the stage and so not visible to the audience

Activity 7

a) Organise these events into the table below, to show which happen on and offstage.

Cathy threatens to gouge out one of Adam's eyes   The gang bully Adam by making him eat leaves

Cathy slaps Brian   Phil picks his teeth   Adam falls down a shaft   Richard walks on his hands

Brian tells the headteacher that a stranger showed him his penis   Leah strangles herself

Leah kills her pet   The police find DNA evidence linking an innocent postman to Adam's death

Phil threatens to kill Brian   Adam is made to 'nick some vodka' *(One, A Wood)*

Jan cries at Adam's memorial

Onstage	Offstage	Reported by

b) In the third column, add the name of the character who reports each offstage action.

c) What do you notice about the things that happen offstage and are reported by the characters?

----

d) Do you think the offstage, reported events increase or decrease tension for the audience? Explain your answer.

Tension

Kelly has used a range of techniques to manipulate the levels of tension for the audience. For example:

- The varying pace of the plot, created through the **juxtaposition** of **monologue**-driven, explorative scenes (such as some of those featuring Leah and Phil) with more urgent, quick-fire dialogue (such as in the exchanges between Jan and Mark).

- Revelations and actions that evoke a strong reaction from the audience, repelling them, shocking them or creating sympathy – for example, when the bullying of Adam is described *(One, A Wood)*.

- Very intense scenes when there is a good deal of **jeopardy** for the characters, such as when John Tate struggles to command the group *(One, A Wood)* and when Adam appears *(Three, A Wood)*.

- Times when characters display high levels of emotion on stage, such as when Leah *'storms off'* *(Three, A Field 2)*.

- Contrasting character reactions and emotions to create drama and humour, such as when Danny obsesses about his dentist career as the group react to what they have done to Adam *(One, A Wood)*.

> **jeopardy** danger of loss, harm or failure
>
> **juxtaposition** placing two opposite ideas or meanings near to or next to each other, to draw attention to the similarities or contrasts between them
>
> **monologue** a long speech given by a single actor with no interruptions from other characters

Activity 8

Select three key lines from the play that you think crank up the tension for the audience and explain why, as in the example provided.

Quotation:

MARK: We need to talk to you.

LEAH: Oh, shit.

(One, A Field)

Explanation: This increases tension because although Mark and Jan introduced the idea of someone being dead in the first scene, the situation wasn't fully explained. Now, after the first long monologue by Leah, which seems to be about other matters, Jan and Mark arrive with their news and Leah's reaction suggests she is anticipating the worst. The audience will expect to find out more.

Quotation: _

_ _

_ _

Explanation: _

_ _

_ _

_ _

_ _

To help find the moments of maximum tension, try focusing on:

- times when information is withheld to create mystery or revealed to create shock or surprise
- cliffhangers at the ends of scenes and episodes, such as in the example given in Activity 8
- moments of intense action
- scenes when characters display high levels of emotion.

Terms for talking about structure

The **external** and **internal structures** of *DNA* are central to its effect on the audience. For example:

- Phil and Leah's **subplot** scenes are mainly static, with Leah musing in monologues on various topics, from evolution (*One, A Field 2*) to **déjà vu** (*Two, A Field*).
- Jan and Mark are always still too, but their dialogue is fast-paced, and they provide **exposition** and act as a commentating **chorus** for the audience.
- Other scenes feature the whole group and have a lot going on, demanding that the audience pay attention to a wide range of speaking and non-speaking characters. An example of this is when Phil comes up with the plot to conceal the group's involvement in Adam's death (*One, A Wood*).
- The stages of the narrative known as the **complication**, the **climax** and the **resolution** are often the most dramatic parts and can have a powerful impact on the audience.

chorus a group that comments on the action of the play

climax the highest point of tension or most intense part of a literary work

complication when the main character's progress is complicated or reversed

déjà vu a feeling of having already experienced the present situation

epiphany a moment when someone suddenly sees or understands something in a new or clearer way

exposition key information about setting, characters and situations, often delivered at an early stage in a literary work

external structure the way a literary work is divided into sections

internal structure the way a story is organised to develop the narrative

resolution the ending of a narrative, where questions are answered and matters are concluded; also known as the denouement

subplot a secondary story told alongside or as part of the main drama

Activity 9

Draw lines to match the following structural features to the examples from *DNA*.

Structural feature	Example from *DNA*
chorus	Phil tells Cathy and Brian to murder Adam
exposition	The story of Phil and Leah's relationship
complication	Jan and Mark's scenes, which comment on events and provide extra information for the audience
climax	'RICHARD: And in that second, Phil, I knew that there was life on other planets.' (Four, A Field)
subplot	The reappearance of Adam
epiphany	The final scene in which Richard takes Leah's place alongside Phil and reveals information about the rest of the group
resolution	The opening scenes that explain the death that begins the story

Upgrade

Make sure you know and understand the terms for talking about structure provided on this page. However, when writing about the play, don't just use the terms as labels. Instead, you will need to incorporate them into your analysis of the play and its impact on the audience.

Writing about plot and structure

The characteristics of some strong and weaker responses to plot are shown below.

Strong answers	Weak answers
Main events of plot referred to and important details picked out	Shows knowledge of main events
Range of comments about how plot links to other aspects of the play, such as tension, character development and atmosphere	Limited comments about how plot links to other aspects of the play, such as tension, character development and atmosphere
Students focus on the question and what the events mean or suggest, using specialist vocabulary	Students do not focus on the question and largely retell the story using their own words

Activity 10

When you write about the play, the examiner will expect you to be able to comment on the significance of events and dialogue, what they symbolise and what layers of meaning they create in the text. You will practise this in the next activity.

a) Read the exam question and extract below. Then read the two student responses on page 15.

b) Use the table on page 13 about strong and weak answers to help you annotate the two answers as if you are the teacher, explaining the strengths and weaknesses of each, and giving advice on improvements where they are needed.

> How does Kelly use reported events in this extract to create tension?

> JAN: So you want us to tell them?
>
> JOHN TATE: Yes! Please.
>
> *He takes his finger away from LEAH'S lips.*
>
> MARK: It's Adam. He's…
>
> I mean we were just having a laugh, weren't we, we were all, you know…
>
> You know Adam, you know what he's like, so we were sort of, well, alright, taking the piss, sort of. You know what he's like he was, sort of hanging around
>
> JAN: Trying to be part of
>
> MARK: Yeah, trying to be part of, yeah, yeah, so we're having a laugh
>
> JAN: with him
>
> MARK: yeah, with him, I mean he's laughing as well, see how far he'll go… We got him to eat some leaves.
>
> JAN: Great big ones, dirty leaves off the floor, he ate them, just like that
>
> MARK: Just like that, we were all
>
> JAN: stitches
>
> MARK: We were in stitches, weren't we
>
> JAN: Adam too, he was
>
> MARK: Oh yeah, Adam was, he was laughing harder than anyone.
>
> JAN Nutter.
>
> MARK: Nutter.
>
> *(One, A Wood)*

Student A

In this scene, Jan and Mark are telling the others what's happened to Adam but they don't do it straight away. Instead of getting to the point – that he is dead – they avoid the truth for a while, by making it sound like it was all 'a laugh' and that Adam was happy to be involved. This means the audience has to wait.

Student B

This scene is part of the exposition of the play, when Jan and Mark are revealing what has happened offstage leading up to the death of Adam. The tension is high for the audience at this point because they know about a death (from the first scene) but not about the details. Kelly creates tension by delaying the crucial revelation about how the boy died, and builds up horror and disgust through the details reported. For example, we imagine poor Adam eating 'dirty leaves off the floor'. The impact on the audience is greater because their revulsion will contrast with the complete lack of humanity shown by Jan and Mark – 'We were in stitches.'

Upgrade

Remember when you are writing essay answers on plot aspects of the text, you will severely limit your marks if you write a simple recount of events. Instead, you need to think carefully about how and why Kelly has constructed and presented scenes in a particular order, and what their effect on the audience is likely to be.

Activity 11

Now try writing about plot and structure again. This time, choose your own extract from one of the group scenes (the Wood sections) to comment on – make sure you select about 15–20 lines in which actions take place or events are revealed. Whichever part of the text you choose, answer this question:

How has Kelly revealed events and actions in these lines and what is their impact on the audience?

Activity 12

Read back over what you have written about the extract you chose in Activity 11 and reflect on the following questions:

- Have you done more than tell the story?
- Have you suggested what actions and events might mean?
- Have you referred to other parts of the play, for example, to make links and comparisons?
- Have you used any specialist vocabulary?
- Have you written about the impact on the audience?
- Do you need to make any changes or try again?

Progress check

Use the table below to review the skills you have developed in this chapter. For each column, start at the bottom box and work your way up towards the highest level in the top box. Tick the box to show you have achieved that level.

I can sustain a critical response to *DNA* and interpret the plot and structure convincingly ☐
I can develop a coherent response to *DNA* and explain the plot and structure clearly ☐
I can make some comments on the plot and structure in *DNA* ☐
Personal response

I can analyse the effects of Kelly's use of language, structure and form in *DNA*, using subject terms judiciously ☐
I can explain how Kelly uses language, structure and form to create effects in *DNA*, using relevant subject terms ☐
I can identify some of Kelly's methods in *DNA* and use some subject terms ☐
Language, structure, form

Context

Understanding context

The **context** of any piece of art can be taken into account to help understand it. In literature, context might include any of the following:

- when a text was written and society's concerns at the time
- events that were happening around the time the text was written and that may have influenced the writing
- ideas that were commonly believed at the time the text was written and how these are relevant to it
- the life and previous writing experiences of the author
- the style and content of other works of literature and art produced at the same time or about similar **themes** or topics, and how these may have influenced the text.

You must avoid filling your exam responses with unexplained or irrelevant facts about the play's context. To gain marks, you need to explain how the context of the play influenced the writing, and its effect on the audience.

Activity 1

Complete the table below by filling the second column with notes about how aspects of the play's context might link to the text. The first row has been started, to show you what is required.

Aspects of the play's context	Link to the text
Dennis Kelly, who has also written successfully for TV, is interested in dark themes and often explores issues facing ordinary people.	The style of the play is **naturalistic** and much of the dialogue in *DNA* is very **colloquial**. This helps to create ordinary-seeming characters and a real-life atmosphere, rather like a TV drama or soap opera.
Kelly says it's difficult to categorise people because very few people are entirely good or entirely bad people; most of us are in the middle of these two extremes.	

Aspects of the play's context	Link to the text
Kelly wrote *DNA* for the National Theatre Connections Festival, which celebrates plays for and about young people.	
The play was written and first performed in the first decade of the 21st century, just after the **Human Genome Project** was completed, while the first conviction of a murderer using DNA evidence was in 1988.	
In 2005, an international climate change agreement came into force, aiming to reduce the causes of global warming.	

colloquial conversational

context the circumstances that form the background for a piece of literature and can help readers to understand it

Human Genome Project an international project to chart the entire genetic material – including all the DNA building blocks – of a human being, completed in 2003

naturalistic created to mirror real life

theme a subject or idea that is repeated or developed in a literary work

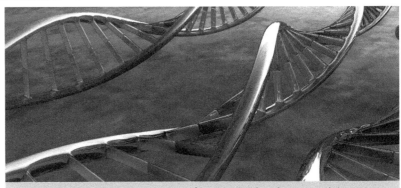

DNA is a substance in the gene part of each cell. It is unique to each human and codes how we look and behave.

Linking context to textual evidence

a) A range of ideas provides additional context to the play. As an introduction to these ideas, complete the middle column in the table below.

Idea	What does this mean and what is its relevance to *DNA*?	Relevant quotations from the text
The story as an **allegory** comparing what happens to Adam to Christ's crucifixion and resurrection in the Bible		
The similarities between humans and other primates such as chimpanzees and bonobos		

Idea	What does this mean and what is its relevance to *DNA*?	Relevant quotations from the text
Different types of bullying and its effects		

b) Read the quotations below and decide which of the ideas in the table they represent. Insert the quotations (or extracts from them) into the correct places on the table.

> 'They murder each other, did you know that? They kill and sometimes torture each other to find a better position within the social structure.'
>
> *(Leah, One, A Field 2)*

> 'And then I came out.
>
> I saw this
>
> light, this daylight light, I saw this light and went that way, towards, and I thought I died...'
>
> *(Adam, Three, A Wood)*

> 'If you go now and you say nothing to no-one about this, you won't be in trouble.'
>
> *(Phil, Three, A Wood)*

c) Now find your own quotations from *DNA* to supplement the ones that were provided for you, and add them to the table.

Upgrade

One reading of *DNA* is that Kelly has created a religious allegory in which Adam represents Christ. Like Christ, Adam was humiliated and tortured until he died, and three days later he rose from the dead. Christians believe Christ's death was for the good of humankind. Do you think Adam's death has any positives?

allegory a work of art that can be interpreted to reveal a hidden spiritual, moral or political meaning

Bullying

One aspect of the social context of *DNA* is how the play explores bullying. Many people reading or attending a performance of the play will have encountered bullies – they may have been bullied, witnessed bullying, reported on bullies or even taken part in bullying behaviour. This means that the audience will come to the play with certain ideas that may be confirmed or challenged by how the play deals with the issue.

Activity 3

Use the following table to record each of the characters' experiences of bullying. Remember to think about ways in which they are victims as well as perpetrators. The first row has been completed as an example.

Character	Experiences of bullying
Leah	Bullied by Phil's silence and feels pressured by her friendship group; accepts shared responsibility for the bullying of Adam; tries to stand up against others but is unable to change their behaviour; shows vicious behaviour towards her own pet
Phil	
Mark	
Jan	
John Tate	
Richard	
Cathy	
Adam	
Lou	
Danny	
Brian	

Read the following extract from one student's work, written in response to this question:

> How does Kelly's exploration of bullying impact on the audience?

Kelly's plays often explore the lives of ordinary people in difficult situations, and some of the types of bullying we see in the play are likely to be familiar to the audience from their own lives and school days. As well as the victimisation of Adam, Phil exerts power over Leah by ignoring her; John Tate expects everyone to admire and obey him because he has given the group authority – 'you can walk down any corridor [...] no-one bothers you'; Cathy controls and abuses Brian. But are all the bullies equal? For example, Cathy is presented as stupid and easily manipulated – she is a victim of bullying as well as becoming someone who 'loves violence now'. As a result, the audience might judge her less harshly than Phil, who orders Cathy to kill Adam with a plastic bag in order to protect himself and the group. Some characters make small efforts to resist the bullying culture but none of them is strong enough to tell an adult or stop the awful chain of events. For instance, Danny argues about John Tate banning the word 'dead', but his main objection to the plan to cover up Adam's death is selfish, because 'Dentists don't get mixed up in things' and he doesn't want to ruin his career plans. The different degrees of bullying and attitudes to bullying that are presented may make the audience think about their own experiences, as well as who deserves the harshest judgement for what happens in the play.

Activity 4

Decide which of the teacher comments below go with which parts of the student's answer.

Highlight the relevant text in the student's response and indicate the appropriate teacher comment by marking it with a number from 1 to 5. Note that some teacher comments are relevant to more than one part of the student's response.

1. Good reference to Kelly's interest in ordinary, real, modern lives

2. Strong use of words and phrases to link points together

3. Good use of embedded quotations from across the text

4. Insightful comparisons between characters

5. Thoughtful comments on the presentation of bullying in the play

Writing about context

Showing a developed understanding of context in the play means linking Kelly's writing choices to the context of his writing. The following activity will help you to do this.

Activity 5

In each of the following examples, the writers are trying to move beyond descriptions of context so that their answers are more analytical. The first student has already been helped by the teacher. Read the teacher's advice for the other examples and then rewrite the student response in the space provided.

Student A
DNA is a naturalistic play about a group of young people who bully another teenager. It was written in the first decade of the 21st century.

This is factually correct, but try to make a stronger link between these contextual facts and how Kelly's writing might have been influenced by them. Also, try to use some short quotations.

Second attempt
DNA, written at the beginning of the 21st century, explores what happens when a group of teenagers take their bullying too far. It is written in a naturalistic style, allowing Kelly to mirror real life and depict themes relevant to all young people – bullying, friendship, morality – in a direct and engaging way.

Student B
In *DNA*, Kelly makes links between the behaviour of supposedly civilised humans and the apes we share 98% of our DNA with.

Well done for describing the context of evolution as an influence on the text. To improve your comment, extend it with an analysis of Leah's monologue about bonobos.

Second attempt

Student C

In *DNA*, there is a bit of a religious context because the character of Adam is a bit like Jesus, who was crucified and then returned from the dead. This is quite effective because it makes you wonder if any good is going to come out of Adam's death.

Second attempt

_____

_____

_____

_____

_____

_____

_____

Your language choices are too informal – express yourself formally in an exam. Also, focus more closely on the effect and impact of the religious context. For example, explore if any of the characters involved in Adam's death have changed by the end of the play.

Progress check

Use the table below to review the skills you have developed in this chapter. For each column, start at the bottom box and work your way up towards the highest level in the top box. Tick the box to show you have achieved that level.

I can sustain a critical response to *DNA* and make analytical comments about its context ☐	I can show a perceptive understanding of how *DNA* is shaped by its context ☐
I can develop a coherent response to *DNA* and explain how its contexts are relevant ☐	I understand the context of *DNA* and can make connections between the text and its context ☐
I can make some comments on the context of *DNA* ☐	I am aware of the context in which *DNA* was written ☐
Personal response	**Text and context**

Character overview

Knowing the characters of any play is an important part of knowing the whole text. In *DNA*, there is a range of characters, but we get to know only Leah in any depth. This is due to her extended monologues, which reveal her innermost thoughts and feelings about many issues – not just what is happening in the play.

Activity 1

a) Complete column 1 in the table by matching a character name from the list below to each description. The first row has been completed as an example.

Phil   Leah   Danny   Adam   Cathy   Lou

Brian   John Tate   Mark   Jan   Richard

Character	Description	Key quotation
Leah	The character we get to know best, through her monologues.	'I talk too much, so shoot me.'
	A junk-food addict, who rarely speaks and often tells everyone else to keep **'their mouths shut'** *(One, A Wood)*.	
	Ambitious and selfish, he is part of the subgroup Phil orders to break in to Adam's house and steal one of his jumpers.	
	An undeveloped character, later described as Cathy's **'best friend'** *(Four, A Field)*.	
	Dangerous and stupid, her love of violence makes her easy to manipulate.	
	Describes Adam's drop into **'the grille'** *(One, A Wood)* and later takes up charity work and shoplifting.	
	Describes how Adam **'burnt his own socks'** *(One, A Wood)* but went home before the stone throwing began.	
	Initially, the leader of the group.	
	Not onstage when Adam reappears, and may not know about his murder.	

Character	Description	Key quotation
	Used to invite the group to his birthday parties.	
	Weak and often seen crying, he's the only character who seems glad when Adam reappears. Later ends up on medication for a mental breakdown.	

b) Complete column 3 in the table by adding a quotation from each character.
Choose from the quotations below. (One is provided for each character.)

'I am brilliant at doing what people say.' *(Three, A Wood)*

'I am trying to keep everyone together.' *(One, A Wood)*

'everyone thinks he's dead. What difference will it make?' *(Three, A Wood)*

'I couldn't remember anything. I was new.' *(Three, A Wood)*

'... I thought, you know, show initiative...' *(Two, A Wood)*

'There are more stars in the universe than grains of sand on Brighton beach.' *(Four, A Field)*

'This is the opposite of Dental college.' *(One, A Wood)*

'... we were just having a laugh.' *(One, A Wood)*

'We're screwed.' *(Two, A Wood)*

'You could tell he was scared.' *(One, A Wood)*

Upgrade

Remember that short quotations are just as powerful as longer ones and are often easier to embed in your own sentences to support your commentary about the play. Look out for key words and phrases that will help to make the same point as a long quotation.

In traditional terms, Phil is the play's **protagonist**, as although he has relatively few lines, he has the most time onstage. However, this play is more of an **ensemble** piece because its impact comes more from the whole cast of characters working as a team than from one or two individual performances.

> **ensemble** a group of musicians, actors or dancers who perform together
> **protagonist** the main character in a work of fiction

Activity 2

To help you think about the cast of characters and how they work together in the play, complete the ranking exercises below. You don't have to include all the characters every time, but try to make sure you include a range so that there are character names at several different positions in each ranking table. Do not count all the lines! Instead, flick through the pages and make a judgement about the characters who are given most and least to say.

a)

	Size of speaking part
Most lines	
Fewest lines	

b)

	Importance to plot
Most important	
Least important	

c)

	Impact on audience
Highest impact	
Lowest impact	

d)

	Likeability
Easiest to like	
Hardest to like	

Activity 3

On separate paper, make a character profile for each of the 11 characters. An example has been completed for you below. Include important information that will help with your revision, such as: name, first appearance onstage, key facts, quotations, relationships and appearance.

Name: Danny

First appearance: *One, A Wood*

Key facts: Wants to be a dentist. Used by Phil as part of the plan to plant false evidence.

Memorable quotation: 'This sort of stuff sticks, you know.' *(Two, A Wood)*

Involvement in what happened to Adam: Was part of the bullying group. Shows no remorse, only wants to avoid being implicated/caught because of his career plans.

Main relationship(s): No particular alliances, though sides with Richard against John Tate. Past tension between him and Cathy (he **'threatened to kill'** her *(Two, A Field)*).

Final appearance: *Two, A Wood*

Exploring characters with evidence

Phil and Leah are the two most significant characters in terms of stage time.

Activity 4

Search through your copy of the text to find evidence to match the following aspects of Phil and Leah. You can write the answers in note form, but try to use a combination of your own words and quotations from the text.

a) Evidence that Phil and Leah are boyfriend and girlfriend:

---

b) Evidence that Phil is clever and highly regarded by the rest of the group:

---

c) Evidence that Phil can be warm and reassuring as well as cold and silent:

---

d) Evidence that Leah is thoughtful, intelligent and curious:

---

e) Evidence that Leah feels a sense of morality or conscience about what happens to Adam:

---

f) Evidence that Phil has changed by the end of the play:

---

g) Evidence that Leah is a well-developed character with different sides to her personality:

Upgrade

If you can show good knowledge of the entire play, your chance of a better grade will be higher. Draw your evidence from a wide range of scenes; from the beginning, middle and end of the play; from the characters' own lines as well as from what others say about them.

Now let's compare another pair of characters – Richard and John Tate.

Activity 5

a) On separate paper, copy and complete the table below to compare John Tate and Richard, following the example provided and using the hints to help.

	John Tate	Richard	Difference (D) or similarity (S)
Name	The only character with a surname. Might indicate his past leadership of the group.	Just like all the characters except John Tate, known only by first name. This reduces their individuality.	D
Status and control			
Relationship with Phil			
Fallout			

b) Now reflect on the completed table and identify in the final column whether you have discovered a difference or similarity between the characters.

c) Using the evidence from the table you've created, write a paragraph comparing John Tate and Richard. You could begin:

> John Tate's surname gives him an extra layer of importance, indicating the bullying way he has led the group in the lead-up to the action of the play. In contrast, Richard is known only by his first name, like all the other characters. This makes Richard more normal and reinforces the idea that he is just another member of the gang. Another difference between the two characters is...

Find Lou's answer to John Tate's question about who she is 'scared of' (One, A Wood) in school.

John Tate doesn't appear in the play after One, A Wood, when he yields control of the group to Phil.

Look at Four, A Field, when Richard reports to Phil on the fallout of the play's events for several characters.

Upgrade

In the exam, you may be called on to compare characters. Rather than just describing similarities and differences, try to comment on them. For example, consider why Kelly made the characters similar or different and how this might enhance the play's impact or affect the audience's reaction.

Linking characters and key ideas

Most characters in *DNA* are linked to key ideas that the play explores; in this way they can be seen as **devices** rather than being fully developed, well-rounded people that we know well and are able to empathise with.

> **device** a technique intended to produce a particular effect or fulfil a purpose in a literary work

Activity 6

a) Use this table to link each character with a key idea explored in the play. Choose from the list of key ideas below the table. Note that several characters can be linked to more than one idea, and the list provided contains more ideas than characters. This means there is no single set of right answers to this activity and you may wish to write more than one idea in each box in the middle column.

b) Use the third column to provide evidence of the links you have made between characters and ideas. The first row has been completed as an example.

Character	Linked to the idea(s) of...	Evidence
Phil	Intelligence and leadership	John Tate says to Phil 'you're clever ... What do we do?'
Leah		
John Tate		
Danny		
Richard		
Cathy		
Brian		
Adam		
Mark and Jan		
Lou		

Ambition   Conscience   Crime   Intelligence   Leadership   Truth

Loyalty   Power   Religion   Status   Violence   Friendship

Shame   Peer pressure   Sacrifice   Belonging   Morality   Deception

Activity 7

Use the table in Activity 6 to help you pick two characters who, in your view, represent the same or linked ideas. Write a paragraph comparing how each character explores those ideas. For example, you might have decided that John Tate and Adam both represent different aspects of religion. You could begin:

> Several characters support the play's exploration of religion. For example, John Tate's reported conversion to 'the Jesus Army' links him to Adam, who describes 'crawling for a long time' towards 'this daylight' as a rebirth...

Upgrade

This is a second opportunity to practise comparing characters, as you did in Activity 5c. Before writing this comparison, read back over your previous comparison attempt and try to improve on it. For example, this time you could:

- develop your comparison by going into more detail
- use more specialist vocabulary
- embed an extra quotation to support your analysis
- make your analysis more thoughtful by commenting on how the comparison between the two characters might impact on the audience.

How characters change

Although we see (or hear about) only a brief period in the characters' lives, we do see them reacting to and dealing with significant and life-changing events. For the audience, the development and transformation of characters helps us to relate to them and recognise them as fellow human beings, each with their own pathway. It's an essential and rewarding part of reading the play or attending a performance.

> **catalyst** something that brings about a change in the story

Activity 8

Use this table to explore the outcome of each character's story.

a) Complete column 1 in the table by writing the name of the correct character alongside each story outcome.

b) In the 'Analysis' column of the table, add a couple of bullet points to comment on the change that the character has undergone, the impact of this on the audience and how it contributes to the overall effect of the play. The entry for Adam has been provided as an example.

Character	Outcome	Analysis
Adam	Survives a life-changing trauma that causes a serious breakdown, disorientation and amnesia but is eventually killed.	• the most dramatic and shocking change for the audience – likely to evoke horror, revulsion, sympathy • **catalyst** that impacts on other characters
	In the final scene, he has lost Leah and *'is not eating'* (Four, A Field), which suggests a huge change. On the other hand, he is unresponsive to Richard as he was to Leah.	
	Finally rejects Phil (**'spits the sweet out'** (Three, A Field 2)) and we then discover that she has moved schools. This demonstrates a sense of guilt and her desire to change.	
	Becomes an active member of a Christian group, suggesting a sense of guilt and a desire to make amends.	
	Remains focused on his career to the end.	
	Becomes more socially involved with the group (**'invited Mark to his party'** (Two, A Field)). At the end, describes an epiphany about **'life on other planets'** (Four, A Field). Seems to widen his understanding of the world.	
	Shows enjoyment of the drama. Becomes more powerful and violent as the play goes on. By the end she is described as **'insane'** (Four, A Field).	
	A weak character to begin with, who is severely affected by his involvement in what happens to Adam. **'They caught him staring at a wall and drooling last week.'** (Four, A Field)	
	Shows some remorse by taking up **'charity work'** (Three, A Field), but remains involved with criminal behaviour and takes up shoplifting.	

Character	Outcome	Analysis
	Moves from the edges of the group to being Cathy's best friend.	
	Shows some remorse with **'floods of tears'** *(Three, A Field)* at Adam's memorial, but remains involved with criminal behaviour and takes up shoplifting.	

Upgrade

Knowing characters well and being able to identify their main actions and key pieces of dialogue is just the basics. You will only access the higher grades by applying this knowledge of character to the exam question and by analysing, for example, how Kelly uses characters to tell the story, how characters compare and contrast, and how characters change and develop.

Comparing characters

Activity 9

This time, you are going to compare the ways in which two characters change or transform. Use your bullet points from the Activity 8 table to help you. You could start like this:

Of course, the most dramatic and shocking change for the audience to come to terms with is what happens to Adam – his humiliation and withdrawal from society, and his eventual death. This is likely to evoke horror and sympathy, especially as most of the other characters seem almost immune to it. The audience may be similarly shocked by what happens to Brian, as he...

Upgrade

When comparing and contrasting, there are some key words and phrases that will come in handy. Try using two or three of these in your comparison about how characters change:

meanwhile	similarly	in contrast

| on the other hand | likewise | in the same way |

| conversely | although | however |

Critical understanding

Reading a text for understanding of characters and relationships means 'reading between the lines' for clues provided by the writer. Not all meanings will be explicit and obvious. Clues may come in the form of the characters' language, tone of voice or actions. These clues will allow you to understand the implicit and subtle meanings of the play.

For example, in the extract that follows, Cathy and Brian have just led Adam out of his hedge hideout. Here we get clues about several different aspects of character.

CATHY: It took me half an hour to get him to come out.

BRIAN: D'you feel how wonderful this day is?

CATHY: I used violence.

BRIAN: She did.

CATHY: I threatened to gouge one of his eyes out.

BRIAN: She was gonna do it. She loves violence now. Can you feel the day licking our skin?

CATHY: He's a mess.

MARK: Which one?

BRIAN: Shall we hold hands? Come on, let's hold, let's hold, let's hold hands, come on, let's –

Suddenly CATHY slaps him.

For a second he looks as if he might cry, but instead he just giggles.

LEAH: Okay. Right. Okay.

Adam.

ADAM: Huh?

LEAH: Hello, Adam. How are you?

ADAM: …

LEAH: Yeah. Great. Phil?

PHIL says nothing.

Because this is a bit… isn't it. I mean this is really, talk about a bolt from the, yeah, shit.

No, not shit, I mean it's good

LOU: Good?

LEAH: it's, yeah, yes it's

JAN: How is it good?

LEAH: it's, it's good, Adam, that found, but I mean yes, it does make things a bit

LOU: Screwed?

(Three, A Wood)

Activity 10

Read the extract carefully and identify the words and phrases that provide the clues for each of the four aspects. The first row has been completed for you.

Brian's childlike nature and pleasure at seeing Adam again	• 'how wonderful this day is' • childish **reiteration** of what Cathy says • 'let's hold hands' • 'looks as if he might cry, but instead he just giggles'
Cathy's violent tendencies	
Leah's moral awareness of the right thing	
Phil's inscrutable or tactical silence	
Lou's simplistic and selfish perspective	

reiteration saying something again, usually to make the point clearer or for emphasis

Upgrade

Note that when collecting evidence about character you need to look throughout the extract and collect all the relevant words and phrases together. This might include what is said, how it is said, stage directions and other characters' reactions.

Writing about characters

Now try independently reading between the lines, this time zooming in on a particular character. First, read the steps below to remind you about how to read closely and effectively, and make notes in preparation for a response to a question.

> **Step 1:** Read once through the extract for general meaning. If you know the play well, you will be able to make this a quick skim read. Remind yourself where in the text the extract comes. Make a note of what has just happened before and what is going to happen next.

> **Step 2:** Reread with a focus. The focus will be determined by the question you are going to answer. Remember to read it and note any key words.

> **Step 3:** Annotate the text with points that are relevant to the question and might help you put together an answer.

 Activity 11

In this activity, the focus is on the character of Leah.

Read the extract opposite from the scene when it is revealed that a stranger has been identified as '**the man who kidnapped Adam**' *(Two, A Wood)*. Use a highlighter to pick out any clues about the character of Leah, and in the space provided around the text, annotate your highlights. Remember to:

- notice what Leah says
- think about how she might say it
- consider what personality traits she reveals
- note how other characters respond to her
- think about the impact on the audience.

An example of a highlight and an annotation has been given.

A Wood. PHIL and LEAH, LOU and DANNY. PHIL has a muffin.
Pause.

LEAH: **What?**

DANNY: They've found…

They…

Well they've found –

LOU: The man.

DANNY: Yeah, they've found the man.

LEAH: They've found the man?

DANNY: Yeah.

LEAH: They've found the man?

DANNY: Yes.

LEAH: Oh my god.

LOU: Exactly.

LEAH: Oh my god.

LOU: That's what we thought, we thought that, didn't we, Danny.

DANNY: Yeah, we did.

LEAH: Are you sure? I mean are you…

DANNY: Definitely. He's in custody now. They're questioning him.

LEAH: But how, I mean who, how, who, who is, who is, how?

LOU: Dunno.

LEAH: Who is he?

LOU: He's the man who kidnapped Adam.

LEAH: Right. No.

LOU: Yes.

LEAH: No.

DANNY: Yes.

LEAH: No, no, yeah, no, actually, because that man, the man who, he doesn't actually, I mean I'm not being fussy or anything, but the man who kidnapped Adam doesn't actually exist, does he. Well does he?

LOU: No. But they've got him.

DANNY: I heard his teeth are awful.

LEAH: You know, I mean he doesn't, he doesn't… Phil? Any… any thoughts? Any words, any comments, any… ideas, any, any, any… thing? At all?

I mean this is, this is, isn't it, this is, is it?

Shit. Oh shit.

(Two, A Wood)

This opening question suggests Leah is impatient or anxious to hear what the others have to say.

Activity 12

You are now going to use the notes you made in Activity 11 to answer a question about Leah, then review what you have written.

a) First, read the success criteria for this activity (see part c, below) and make sure you are familiar with the expectations of the task.

b) Write a paragraph answering the following question:

> How does Kelly reveal Leah's character in this scene?

Use the annotations you made in Activity 11, and remember to refer to the text you have highlighted – it should provide words and phrases you can embed as quotations in your answer.

---

c) Review your writing about Leah and use a tick or a cross to mark it against these success criteria.

Success criteria	My work
Demonstrates knowledge of Leah's character in this scene	
Comments on Kelly's portrayal of Leah (e.g. what Leah says, how she might say it, what personality traits she reveals, how others react to her)	
Comments on the impact of Leah's character on the audience (e.g. the emotions Leah's words and behaviour might evoke, how they might compare or contrast Leah with other characters, how they might judge Leah)	
Some specialised vocabulary (e.g. dialogue, onstage, offstage, questions, **repetition**)	
Refers to other important scenes featuring Leah and therefore shows wider knowledge of the play	

repetition repeated words, phrases, ideas and structures

Progress check

Use the table below to review the skills you have developed in this chapter. For each column, start at the bottom box and work your way up towards the highest level in the top box. Tick the box to show you have achieved that level.

I can sustain a critical response to *DNA* and interpret the characters convincingly ☐	I can use well-integrated textual references from *DNA* to support my interpretation ☐	I can analyse the effects of Kelly's use of language, structure and form in *DNA*, using subject terms judiciously ☐
I can develop a coherent response to *DNA* and explain the characters clearly ☐	I can use quotations and other textual references from *DNA* to support my explanation ☐	I can explain how Kelly uses language, structure and form to create effects in *DNA*, using relevant subject terms ☐
I can make some comments on the characters in *DNA* ☐	I can make references to some details from *DNA* ☐	I can identify some of Kelly's methods in *DNA* and use some subject terms ☐
Personal response	**Textual references**	**Language, structure, form**

Technical terms

The key aspects of the language of *DNA* are explored in this chapter. First, check you understand the key terms you will need to use to write about language.

Activity 1

Draw a line from each term to its definition in the other column. The first answer has been provided for you.

Terms	Definitions
Colloquial	Incomplete sentences
Duologue	Indications from the playwright about how scenes should be presented or words should be spoken
Dialogue	A style of writing that mirrors a character's continuous, unedited thoughts
Filler words	Empty words (such as 'like', 'you know', 'just') that carry no meaning but are often used in normal conversation
Ellipsis	Swearing
Expletives	Omission of words that are nevertheless able to be understood due to context *or* the three dots used to show when a character's sentence trails off
Hesitation	A slight pause
Interruptions	A style of writing that mirrors a character's continuous, unedited thoughts
Monologue	A long speech given by a single actor with no interruptions from other characters
Monosyllabic	Conversational
Repetition	Speech between two characters
Sentence fragments	Made up of words of single syllables
Stage directions	Repeated words, phrases, ideas and structures
Stream of consciousness	Speech between any number of characters

Upgrade

In the exam, you will be expected to use some specialist terminology correctly to refer to how language is used in the play. However, you must avoid the simple 'naming of parts' and your writing must include analysis of how the writer has used language, its effects and impact.

Language features

The following language features occur throughout the play.

1. Expletives and swearing – mirroring teenagers' everyday language; swearing in the play is a shorthand way for the characters to express strong feelings – for example, of fear, anger, disgust or shock.

2. Repetition and echoing – sometimes drawing attention to an important word or idea; sometimes part of the characters' inarticulate expression.

3. Filler words – words that give the speaker 'thinking time' or improve the flow of conversation; usually removed from formal talk but used in the play to help create a colloquial, informal style.

4. Sentence fragments and unfinished sentences help to suggest that characters' talk is not planned and that they are saying the first thing that comes into their heads.

5. Interruptions – often indicated by dashes; sometimes characters interrupt themselves (breaking off from one topic to suggest they are really thinking about something else) and sometimes they interrupt each other, which helps to create fast-paced, naturalistic, informal exchanges.

6. Monosyllabic words and lines – exchanges of one-syllable words can create a swift pace and are also used to convey a simplistic, unthinking or confused response.

Activity 2

Enter 1–6 to show where the language features in the list above occur in the following extract from *One, A Wood*.

A wood. LOU, JOHN TATE and DANNY.

LOU: Screwed.

JOHN TATE: No, no, it's not, no, Lou, we're not

LOU: We are screwed.

JOHN TATE: No, Lou, we're not…it's not…we're not… nothing's….

LOU: It is.

JOHN TATE: No, no, no, look, there I have to, I really have to, you're going to have to listen to me on this one, and you are going to have to believe me. Everything is, everything's fine.

LOU: Fine?

JOHN TATE: Not fine, no

DANNY: Fine?

JOHN TATE: not fine exactly, alright, fair enough, I mean things are bad, things are a little, alright, yes, I'm not trying to hide the, this is tricky, it's a tricky

LOU: Tricky?

JOHN TATE: situation, but it's not, because actually what you are saying is a very negative, and that's…

Look, haven't I looked after things before?

LOU: This is different.

JOHN TATE: Lou, are you scared of anyone in this school?

> LOU: You?
>
> JOHN TATE: Apart from me.
>
> LOU: No.
>
> JOHN TATE: Exactly
>
> LOU: Richard, maybe
>
> JOHN TATE: exactly, that's exactly, that's what I'm saying – Richard, you're scared of, are you…? – I mean you can walk down any corridor in this – I don't think Richard's – any corridor in this school and you know, no-one bothers you and if you want something it's yours and no-one bothers you and everyone respects you and everyone's scared of you and who made that, I mean I'm not boasting, but who made that happen?
>
> LOU: You.
>
> JOHN TATE: Thank you, so are things really that bad?
>
> LOU: Yes.
>
> JOHN TATE: Richard? I mean are you really?
>
> *(One, A Wood)*

Activity 3

In the following student answer about the same extract from *One, A Wood*, the technical terms have been omitted. Insert each term (see margin) in the right place to create an answer with a good balance of specialist vocabulary and analysis.

contractions   dashes   echoes   **monosyllables**   naturalistic   questioning   repeat   sentence fragments

In DNA, Kelly has carefully crafted an impression of _____ dialogue in order to make the characters and situations seem as real as possible. The vocabulary is usually simple and the _____ help to mirror informal talk. In this extract, when John Tate tries to reassure Lou and Danny that things are not really 'that bad', the characters often speak in _____ ('you'/'yes'/'screwed'), creating a fast exchange of words and the impression of a typical teenage conversation. At a different point, we see John Tate's surprise and distraction when Lou reveals that she feels scared of Richard, and this is shown by the _____ and _____ in his speech. Elsewhere, the characters _____ each other's lines, like when Danny _____ the word 'fine' with a _____ tone. This is also very commonplace in ordinary conversation, as well as hinting at John Tate's loss of authority, which follows soon.

Crafting reality

A fundamental aspect of *DNA* is the colloquial style. However, the apparently natural and realistic tone is actually carefully crafted to help the audience view the characters as 'normal' teenagers, who talk in ways we recognise from real life.

- They sometimes don't speak in whole sentences – often they don't need to, as they understand each other well.

- They interrupt each other a lot and finish each other's sentences.

- They repeat each other (sometimes for emphasis, sometimes to challenge or question).
- They are sometimes inarticulate.
- They often pause or hesitate.
- They insult each other and swear.

The fact that the teenage characters never have to interact with adults – which might make them adapt their language to be more formal or polite – helps to immerse the audience in their world.

So, Dennis Kelly has constructed the characters' exchanges to make us believe that they are just saying the first thing that comes into their heads at any given moment. Of course, the reality is that the actors playing the cast will have learned the lines extremely carefully – then they just have to deliver the lines in a way that makes them sound fresh and natural.

Activity 4

Identify three short quotations from across the play that illustrate some of the ways the play mirrors the language of real life.

	Example from One	Example from Two	Example from Three
Colloquial language			
Stream of consciousness			
Ellipsis (…)			
Ellipsis (omission of words)			

contraction the shortening of a word or phrase, for example, by replacing one or more letters with an apostrophe (you're, I'm)

ellipsis omission of words that are nevertheless able to be understood due to context *or* the three dots used to show when a character's sentence trails off

monosyllables single syllables

stream of consciousness a style of writing that mirrors a character's continuous, unedited thoughts

The apparently natural language of *DNA* is partly achieved through another feature of everyday conversation – overlapping lines. This happens, for example, when:

- one character speaks continuously but other characters interrupt or speak over their lines
- characters echo each other and complete each other's sentences.

Key quotation

Jan: Nutter.

Mark: Nutter.

Jan: complete

Mark: complete nutter

(One, A Wood)

Another significant feature in *DNA* is Dennis Kelly's use of pauses, **hesitations** and beats.

Key quotation

Everyone's scared.

S'not just me.

Pause.

We've got each other.

We need each other.

So don't give it all…

You need me as much as…

Don't give it all the…

Beat.

What are you thinking?

(Leah, One, A Field)

Activity 5

Consider the statements below. Underneath each one, state whether you agree or disagree and make a comment about why. The first one has been done as an example.

a) The pauses help the dialogue in the play to sound natural.

> Agree – this is part of the writer's approach to make the whole play feel very real and the characters seem ordinary.

b) Pauses and silences onstage could help to create tension for the audience.

---

c) If there is a pause in dialogue onstage, it will give the audience a chance to look at all the characters.

----

d) A silence in the middle of a scene might make the audience think the actors have forgotten their lines.

----

e) Pauses, beats and hesitations might make the audience feel uncomfortable.

Activity 6

Reread Part Four of the play and identify a quotation to illustrate the language features listed in the table below.

Language feature	Quotation from Part Four
Sequence of monosyllabic lines	
Pause	
Colloquial language	
Characters echoing each other	
Silence	
Polysyllabic speech	

polysyllabic made up of more than one syllable
hesitation a slight pause

Characters and different language styles

Although the play is mostly written in informal language and many language features are used by all of the characters, there are also differences in the way the characters speak. These differences are used to emphasise different themes in the play, such as violence and power, and to signal the characters' varying degrees of:

- intelligence

- status and authority

- distress.

Activity 7

a) Complete the table below.
  i.   Fill in the middle column with the speaker's name from the list, adding the scene in which the quotation appears.
  ii. Match the commentaries provided to each speaker. The first row has been done for you.

Quotation	Speaker and scene	Commentary number
Dead? Yeah. What, dead?	Jan and Mark One, A Street	2
I'm in charge. Everyone is happier. What's more important; one person or everyone?		
D'you ever want to rub your face against the earth? I love this! This is great! Mates!		
He answers the description. Fat postman, thinning hair, his teeth are terrible, apparently.		
Imagine being inside a cloud, but with space inside it as well, for a second, as I was coming up here I felt like I was an alien in a cloud.		
dark place and I don't remember things I fell, I falled into, I fell onto this…		

Jan and Mark   Brian   Richard   Phil   Danny   Adam

1 This character often speaks with intelligence and authority. He tends to use whole sentences and not be interrupted by others. In this quotation, he is taking on Leah's role with the silent Phil, musing about the world and a strange experience.

2 In their 'Street' scenes, both these characters speak mainly in monosyllables. Their talk, as in this quotation, is characterised by one-word exchanges, brief statements, repetitions and questions, which makes them seem paralysed by their inability to do anything outside of the group.

3 This character is well-spoken and his remarks often reveal his aspirations for the future. In this quotation, like elsewhere, his comment introduces a note of dark humour, as his obsession with his career plans comes through even at the most inappropriate moments.

4 This character says what he's thinking and is direct about his emotions. In the later stages of the play his speech is affected by prescribed drugs. In the scene quoted, his odd questions and childish exclamations show that he fails to understand the seriousness of the situation; he simply seems excited to see his friend again.

5 This character speaks in broken phrases and his speeches are presented in a fragmented way on the page, reflecting his traumatic experience. In this quotation, his inability to find and use the correct words suggests an emotional, mental and language breakdown.

6 This character seldom speaks, but when he does he takes charge. He is articulate, speaks in full sentences and comes up with clever plans. Others always listen to him. This quotation sums up a moral dilemma at the heart of the play.

b) Now fill in a table, similar to the one on page 48 for the remaining characters: Leah, Cathy, Lou and John Tate, adding in the scene. Try to model the comments in the third column on the ones in the speech bubbles above, showing how the language of the characters reflects what they are like or their role in the play.

Quotation	Speaker and scene	Commentary
	Leah	
	Cathy	
	Lou	
	John Tate	

Writing about language choices

You now know the play well and have the technical terms to talk about its language. In the previous activity you began developing comments about the characters' speaking styles and how this is represented on the page. Now it's time to bring this learning together to analyse Kelly's language choices more independently.

foreshadow to warn by mentioning in advance

 Activity 8

a) Look at the table below. Locate the quotations from Leah's speeches in the play and write the part number and setting in the middle column.

b) Reread the text leading up to and just after each quotation. Then, in the middle column again, write a note about what is literally happening at this point. This will remind you of the context of each quotation.

c) In the third column, write a comment on the language techniques being used. Try to embed a word or phrase from the quotation into your comment, as in the example given.

Think about the violence of Leah's vocabulary here and how it **foreshadows** events and ideas from later in the play

Look at the punctuation showing the lack of fluency here and think about the difference between this speech and the style of Leah's monologues

Quotation	When this is and what's happening	Comment on language
...so don't start Phil, don't come here giving it all the, you know, all the, all the... *Beat*. Can you remember the happiest moment in your life?	*Two, A Field* Leah is talking while Phil eats sweets. She has just been talking about the 'beauty and fragility of reality' and is about to show Phil her dead pet.	At this point, mid-monologue, Leah becomes unusually inarticulate, repeating herself and being unable to complete her sentence. This leads to a moment of silence, which suggests the emotional distance between the two characters. A grim type of humour is introduced when she tells Phil 'don't start', as the audience understands that silent Phil is very unlikely to do so.
So kill me, Phil, call the police, lock me up, rip out my teeth with a pair of rusty pliers, I talk too much, what a crime, what a sin, what an absolute catastrophe, stupid, evil, ridiculous ...		
Because he's mad! We can't leave him here, I mean that's not, are you serious? Are you seriously – Alright, yes, there'll be – Phil, this is insane.		

Learn some short quotations that have interesting language features, which you may be able to use in your exam response. You will need to memorise the speaker too. Remember that short quotations can be as effective as longer ones.

Upgrade

Analysing repetition

Repetition is a significant language feature in the play, as well as being important structurally.

Activity 9

a) Look at the uses of repetition in column 1 in the table below. Do they relate to the play's structure, to its language or to both? Write your answer in column 2.

b) Match the uses of repetition to the correct analysis by drawing lines from columns 1 and 2 to column 3.

Uses of repetition	Structure, language or both?	Analysis
The scene settings are repeated (street, field, wood, field; street, field, wood, field).	both	Act as a type of chorus, commenting on the action.
The word 'dead' and related words such as 'died' and 'kill' are repeated.		Mimics the pattern of everyday conversation; suggests characters are stuck in the situation they've created as some talk goes round in circles.
There are numerous references to religion in the form of the words 'God', 'Jesus' and 'Christ'.		Reference the wider world and big ideas that inform the play, as well as introducing a note of humour as the audience begins to predict how each character will behave.
Scenes featuring only Jan and Mark, in the street, occur four times.		Suggests that the characters are stuck in an unpleasant cycle of events in a very ordinary world and can't escape.
Scenes in which Leah speaks in monologues to a silent Phil occur six times.		Reinforces the main plot point and creates a very dark atmosphere.
Characters frequently echo each other's words.		Create a Christian context for the play and remind the audience of other relevant Christian concepts such as crucifixion, forgiveness and sin.

Read the notes below, made by a student preparing to answer the question:

> How does Kelly use language to show conflict?

- Conflict between characters most obvious in Wood scenes when there are several onstage at once
- Use example of when Cathy reveals she has 'got DNA evidence' to frame an innocent man – she is in conflict with everyone here as shown by her unique excitement ('it was great')
- Mention echoing – Danny and Lou both say 'Oh my god' but this doesn't suggest they are united
- Danny reveals his selfish concerns ('can't be mixed up in something like that')
- Refer to beats and pauses, which show another's disbelief and shock
- Comment on how Leah tries to understand ('Right. Okay. Hang on. Where did you get the DNA evidence?') but this leaves her sounding unusually inarticulate
- Compare this moment to other conflicts (e.g. Leah's reaction when Phil demonstrates to Cathy how to murder someone with a plastic bag)

Activity 10

Using the notes above, complete the student answer.

> An example of conflict in DNA occurs when Cathy reveals what she has done to frame an innocent man. Uniquely, and putting her in conflict with everyone else, she is excited about getting 'on the telly' and describes the situation as 'great'. In contrast...

Activity 11

Assess the strengths and weaknesses of your paragraph, referring to the bullet list below. Annotate your writing to highlight possible improvements, then write a final draft on a separate sheet of paper.

- Stays focused on the idea of conflict ☐
- Gives examples from the text ☐
- Uses some specialist vocabulary ☐
- Embeds quotations ☐
- Links ideas together with cohesive devices (e.g. in contrast, however, on the other hand) ☐
- Refers to more than one part of the play ☐
- Accurate and formal writing, expressing ideas clearly ☐

Progress check

Use the table below to review the skills you have developed in this chapter. For each column, start at the bottom box and work your way up towards the highest level in the top box. Tick the box to show you have achieved that level.

Personal response	Language, structure, form
I can sustain a critical response to *DNA* and interpret the language convincingly ☐	I can analyse the effects of Kelly's use of language, structure and form in *DNA*, using subject terms judiciously ☐
I can develop a coherent response to *DNA* and explain Kelly's use of language clearly ☐	I can explain how Kelly uses language, structure and form to create effects in *DNA*, using relevant subject terms ☐
I can make some comments on the language features of *DNA* ☐	I can identify some of Kelly's methods in *DNA* and use some subject terms ☐

Key ideas

Kelly explores several themes in the play and it's important to have a good understanding of them.

Activity 1

Consider the following spider diagram of some of the play's themes and identify a relevant moment from the text for each one. Write a short note about the moment you have chosen, using the completed example as a guide.

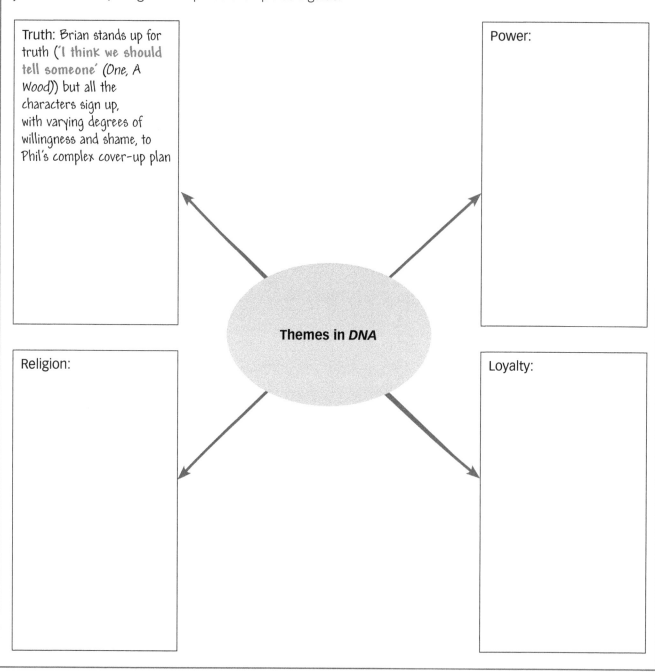

Truth: Brian stands up for truth ('I think we should tell someone' (One, A Wood)) but all the characters sign up, with varying degrees of willingness and shame, to Phil's complex cover-up plan

Power:

Religion:

Loyalty:

Themes in *DNA*

When exploring the themes of a piece of literature, always be aware that it is likely to explore related or opposite ideas too. For example, the fact that *DNA* is about truth, and related ideas of reality and certainty, means that it is also about lies, and related ideas of unreliability and deception.

Activity 2

Use the space provided to group the following words into clusters of ideas that show how the themes of the play are not one-dimensional. You can make as many clusters of ideas as you like, and use separate paper if you need to.

One cluster has been formed for you. Note that some groups of ideas may be bigger than others and that you may want to use some of the words more than once, as they may link together in different ways.

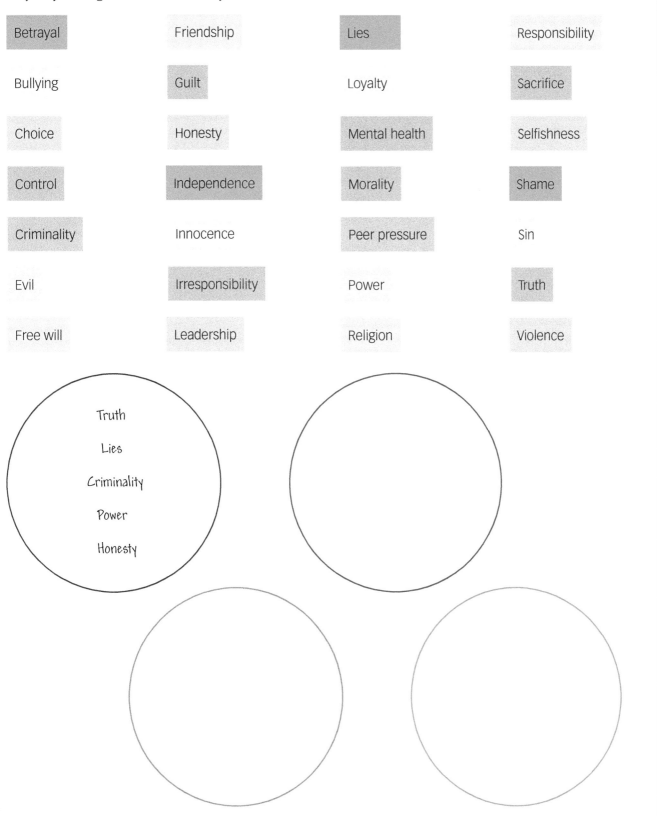

Betrayal	Friendship	Lies	Responsibility
Bullying	Guilt	Loyalty	Sacrifice
Choice	Honesty	Mental health	Selfishness
Control	Independence	Morality	Shame
Criminality	Innocence	Peer pressure	Sin
Evil	Irresponsibility	Power	Truth
Free will	Leadership	Religion	Violence

Truth

Lies

Criminality

Power

Honesty

Finding evidence for themes

Creating a bank of quotations to help you explore the main themes in the text is a good idea. Rereading the text, as you will need to in the next activity, will make sure you know it really well and give you a great advantage when you have to write about it.

Activity 3

For each theme in the table on page 57, complete the following.

a) Add a relevant quotation from this selection to the second column of the table.

Quotation 1

JAN: That's when I went home

MARK: anything, yeah, only because you had to.

JAN: I wasn't there when –

(One, A Wood)

Quotation 2

JOHN TATE: Are you on my side? With Richard and Danny? Are you on our side, Cathy?

(One, A Wood)

Quotation 3

PHIL: Richard, you take Brian to the Head, tell him that you found Brian crying in the toilets, asked him what was wrong and when he told you, you brought him here.

(One, A Wood)

Quotation 4

BRIAN: I can't face it. They look at me. They look at me like I'm lying and it makes me cry.

(Two, A Wood)

Quotation 5

LEAH: They murder each other, did you know that? They kill and sometimes torture each other to find a better position within the social structure.

(One, A Field 2)

Quotation 6

RICHARD: John Tate's found god [...] He's joined the Jesus Army, he runs round the shopping centre singing and trying to give people leaflets.

(Four, A Field)

Quotation 7

LEAH: Oh, great, now you're talking to Cathy, like, I'm not, I'm not, because you don't like what I say and now it's Cathy, you sit there and you say nothing for years and suddenly now you chatting with Cathy.

(Three, A Wood)

b) Skim through the play to find your own quotation to go with each idea and enter it in the third column.

Theme	Quotation from list provided	Further quotation (find this independently)
Truth and lies		
Power		
Loyalty		
Religion		
Guilt and responsibility		
Morality		
Peer pressure		

Upgrade

As well as showing your close knowledge of the text, embedding short quotations in your own writing is a good way to save time (you don't want to spend time remembering or writing out massive sections of the play). Use a highlighter to identify the key word or a short phrase that could be embedded in your own writing from each of the quotations you've inserted in the table for Activity 3.

Linking themes

As we found out in Activity 2, many of the ideas in *DNA* are intertwined. For example, you can start off looking at the idea of bullying, which might lead you to the theme of power and then to the notion of responsibility.

We could show this in a flow diagram:

Bullying is a key theme in the play. The main action involves the extreme bullying of Adam, and it is also explored in Cathy's treatment of Brian, and Phil's authority and *power* over the group.

⬇

Phil's *power* is linked to his intelligence – this allows him to take over when John Tate, a leader at first, is too weak to take command in the face of Adam's first 'death'. Once Phil's plan is put in place, it is perhaps inevitable that the others will continue to look to him and that he will take ultimate *responsibility* for the survival of the group.

⬇

Arguably, Phil shows strength of character by taking *responsibility* in this way, but it does seem to have an impact on him: by the end of the play, he is reduced to *'staring at nothing'* and won't leave *'that stupid field'* (Four, A Field), despite Richard's attempts at persuasion.

Activity 4

Use the templates provided to create your own flow diagrams to show how ideas link together. You can insert your own choice of theme trios, or use these suggested ideas:

Bullying ⟶ Criminality ⟶ Morality

Peer pressure ⟶ Loyalty ⟶ Choice

> [blank box]

⬇

> [blank box]

⬇

> [blank box]

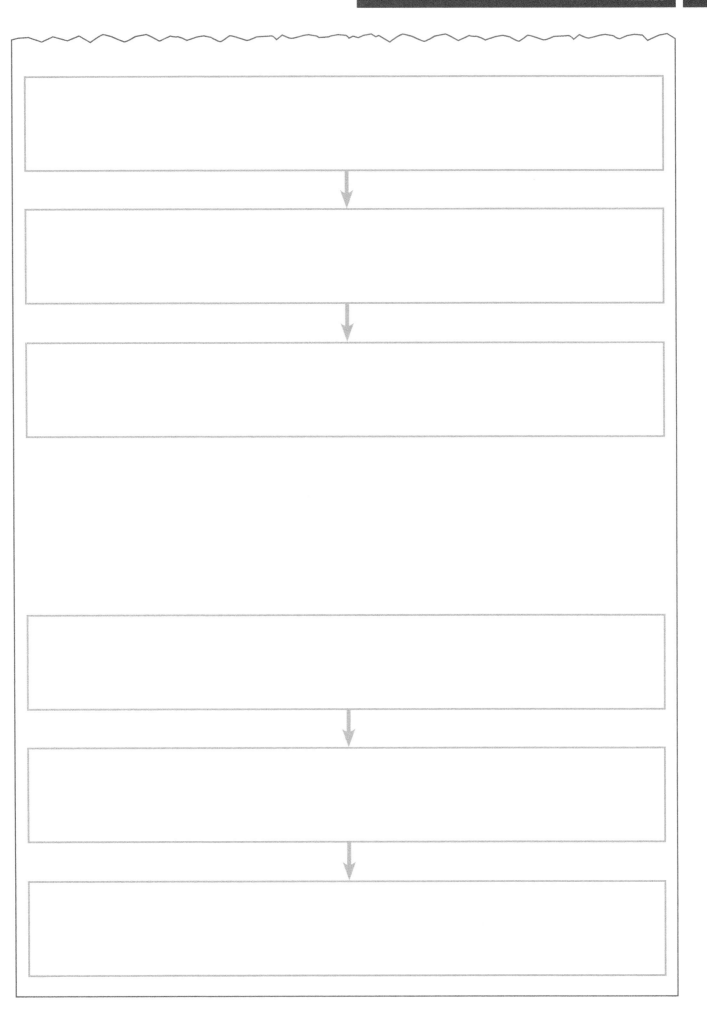

Recognising and tracking themes

Remember that themes are ideas that crop up again and again in a text. They are usually introduced in the early pages, and then referred to and developed as the play goes on. However, they may not always be obvious – Kelly may represent the ideas in different ways, through characters and events or actions.

Activity 5

Match the events or actions listed on the left with the theme each stands for on the right, as in the example shown. One is done as an example.

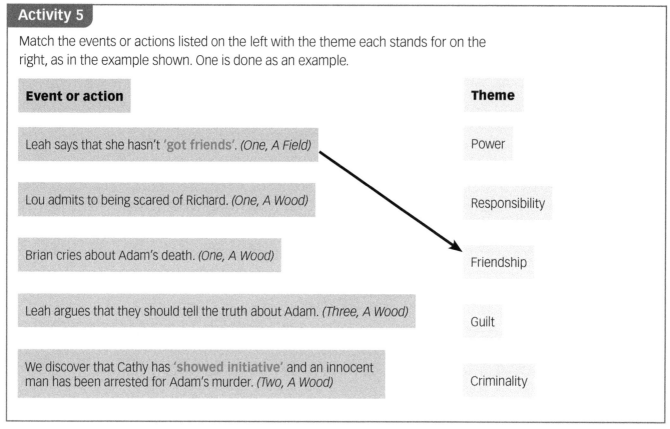

Event or action		Theme
Leah says that she hasn't **'got friends'**. *(One, A Field)*		Power
Lou admits to being scared of Richard. *(One, A Wood)*		Responsibility
Brian cries about Adam's death. *(One, A Wood)*		Friendship
Leah argues that they should tell the truth about Adam. *(Three, A Wood)*		Guilt
We discover that Cathy has **'showed initiative'** and an innocent man has been arrested for Adam's murder. *(Two, A Wood)*		Criminality

Tracking themes as they develop scene by scene should be an important element of your revision of the text, because it will reinforce your understanding that the ideas are not static or simplistic. For example, you want to move away from a simple statement, such as 'Kelly explores the idea of loyalty in the play', to instead make a more thoughtful comment, such as 'Kelly presents loyalty as complex, exploring how it is easily damaged by fear, self-interest and guilt'.

Activity 6

Choose three themes and find references to them in at least three different scenes.
Make brief notes about each reference in the table below and on the next page,
focusing on how that idea or theme is developed. One example has been completed
as a guide. Try to embed a relevant quotation in your commentary if you can.

Themes	References
Loyalty	1. In One, A Street, we meet Jan and Mark. Their loyalty to each other is evident in the way they immediately share the problem of Adam's death, and clarify together there has been 'no mistake', 'it's not funny' and Adam is 'not hiding'. Their loyalty is also shown in the use of the pronoun 'we' in the final line of the scene. 2. In One, A Field 2, Leah compares the loyalty of humans, chimpanzees and bonobos. Bonobos are the most loyal, she implies, because 'they'll all look sad' if another of their group is in pain. 3. In Four, A Street, we see a demonstration of Jan and Mark's loyalty to each other – they are still friends. On the other hand, Leah, they state, has 'gone'. Leah's loyalty to Phil was strong but ultimately she rejected him after his inhuman behaviour towards Adam.
	1.
	2.
	3.

Themes	References
	1.
	2.
	3.
	1.
	2.
	3.

Interpreting ideas

Once you know how to track the development of ideas, you will be able to write effectively and analytically about Kelly's themes. For example, here is the beginning of a sample student answer to the question:

> How does Kelly present ideas about bullying?

The teacher's comments show the strengths of this piece of writing.

Effective use of key word from the title and a range of related ways to refer to the theme.

Comment on use of language – well done.

Good – a brief reference to the plot without retelling the story.

Bullying is at the heart of this play and present in many forms. For example, in Leah and Phil's relationship, although they are apparently equals, Phil's silence humiliates Leah as she tries to get him to respond and becomes increasingly frustrated. In the first group scene (One, A Wood) we see a leadership battle between different bullies – John Tate, Richard and Phil – competing for control of the group. John Tate's tactics – banning words and reminding the others how he has 'looked after things before' – prove ineffective. Unlike John Tate, Richard remains unflustered, and speaks in grammatically correct whole sentences, challenging John Tate's right to 'threaten me'. However, Richard doesn't appear to want control – 'I want to say nothing, just like you'. Phil then emerges as the ultimate bully. His clever plan and cool instructions – 'Get in, go to his bedroom, find a pair of his shoes' – reveal a cold and calculating mentality that arguably reaches a dramatic peak for the audience in the shocking plastic bag scene. At this point, Phil dehumanises Brian completely, turning him into a mannequin in the demonstration of how Cathy must complete the destruction of Adam.

A range of words and phrases used to connect points and signal the direction of the argument.

Relevant quotations embedded.

Excellent comment on the author's intentions.

Activity 7

Use one of the following question templates to write your own question around a theme – you just need to insert the theme you want to write about in the space.

- What are Kelly's ideas about _____ and how does he show its different sides?

- How does the theme of _____ impact on the audience?

- Referring to three different scenes, explain how the play explores the theme of _____.

Activity 8

Write the opening paragraph of an answer to the question you created in Activity 7. Try to incorporate the strengths of the writing in the student answer on page 63. Continue on separate paper if you need to.

Activity 9

Review the writing you did in response to Activity 8. For each of the success criteria in the table below, find an example to prove that you met this requirement then give yourself a mark out of 10 for that aspect in the final column. Be honest with yourself – over-inflating your marks at this point will only lead to you being less well prepared for your exam.

Criteria	Example from my work	Mark /10
Effective use of key words from the question/a range of related ways to refer to the theme		
A brief reference to the plot without retelling the story		
Relevant quotations embedded		
Comment on use of language		
Comment on the author's intentions		
A range of words and phrases used to connect points and signal the direction of the argument		

Progress check

Use the table below to review the skills you have developed in this chapter. For each column, start at the bottom box and work your way up towards the highest level in the top box. Tick the box to show you have achieved that level.

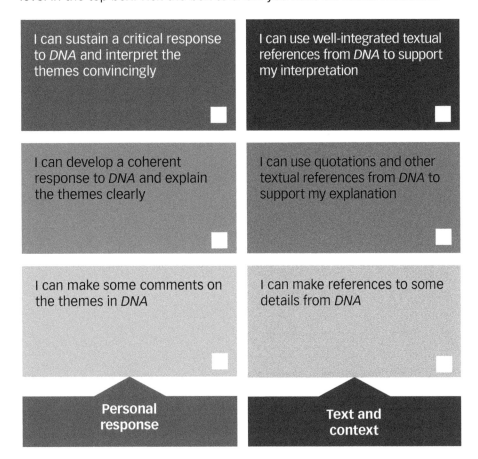

Personal response	Text and context
I can sustain a critical response to *DNA* and interpret the themes convincingly ☐	I can use well-integrated textual references from *DNA* to support my interpretation ☐
I can develop a coherent response to *DNA* and explain the themes clearly ☐	I can use quotations and other textual references from *DNA* to support my explanation ☐
I can make some comments on the themes in *DNA* ☐	I can make references to some details from *DNA* ☐

Performance

Staging the play

Putting on a production of any play is a collaboration, with a team of people involved. In small drama companies, some people might do more than one of these jobs, while in bigger groups there will be more people to take on individual roles.

Activity 1

Match each of the following roles to the job descriptions provided below.

Team member	Role description
Writer	Responsible for the lighting and sound and other technical and backstage requirements during each performance
Designer	Develops a vision of the play, casts the actors in their roles, interprets the play from page to stage, directs the actors in the performance space, works with the actors to develop characters
Actors	Writes the play, creates the characters, imagines the settings
Director	Manages the finances, including the marketing
Producer	Work with the director to develop their characters through their lines, tone of voice, and **non-verbal communication**, including gestures and movement around the stage, facial expressions, eye contact, use of **props**, body language and reactions to others
Stage manager	Creates the set, costumes, lighting and sound

non-verbal communication communication without words
props moveable objects used onstage by the actors

Activity 2

a) Look at the list of props and costume items in the table on page 67, and match them to either Adam, Leah, Brian or Phil by inserting the correct name in the middle column.

b) In the third column, write a note about what the prop or costume item represents or is used to show onstage. The first row has been completed as an example.

Item	Character	
Plastic container	Leah	This is the box that Leah has her dead pet in. When she shows it to Phil, it represents her own random act of violence, her desperate attempt to get Phil to respond to her and her struggle to understand herself. It also underlines the theme of power and violence, showing that even the most thoughtful and empathetic of the characters is capable of extreme behaviour.
Waffle		
Suitcase		
Torn, dirty clothes		
Earth (to eat)		
Carrier bag		

Upgrade

Remember that every aspect of the play has been thought through and is intended to convey meaning to the audience. For example, even though Phil's choice of junk food may seem incidental, there is a difference between the way he eats sweets in *Two, A Field 1* – one by one, perhaps lovingly unwrapping each one – and the way he prepares (but never gets to eat) his waffle in *Three, A Field 1*. When writing about the play, always think about what the props represent and the extra layers of meaning they can communicate to the audience.

Although other places – including a school, a police station, Adam's house and a shopping centre – are mentioned in the play, none of these have to be represented onstage. All the action takes place in a street, a field and a wood, and each of these settings is anonymous and generic: Kelly does not describe them in any detail, so they could be anywhere, in any town or part of the country.

Activity 3

Consider the following statements that other students have made about the play's settings and say whether you agree or disagree, adding a comment to explain your view.

a) The wood is the most important setting.

I agree/disagree because _____

_____

b) Kelly chose the 'street' setting because teenagers traditionally hang around on streets.

I agree/disagree because _____

_____

c) The street in this play is strange and not very believable because it is always empty apart from Jan and Mark.

I agree/disagree because _____

_____

d) The settings are random: it wouldn't matter if Phil and Leah were always in the street, Jan and Mark's scenes took place in the wood, and the group scenes happened in the field.

I agree/disagree because _____

_____

e) The three settings aren't described in detail, so it is easy for the audience to believe that this story could happen anywhere.

I agree/disagree because _____

_____

f) Even though it's a short play and the scenes alternate fast between the three settings, I still think the street, the field and the wood should be as detailed as possible.

I agree/disagree because _____

_____

Most directors would disagree with statement f): creating detailed sets to represent a street, a wood and a field would involve building backdrops and creating lamp posts, shop fronts, trees and bushes. As well as being time-consuming and expensive, this might also detract from the action of the play – think of all the time the audience would have to sit and wait for new sets and props to be put in place! Instead, most directors putting on this play have chosen to use lighting, projections, sound and minimal props to distinguish each setting.

Activity 4

Imagine you are co-directing a new production of *DNA*. You have the following equipment:

- a **lighting rig** and a range of different coloured lights and spotlights
- a **cyclorama**
- a projector
- a **floor cloth**
- a sound-effects machine
- a bench.

cyclorama a cloth or screen stretched tight to form the back wall of a stage set

floor cloth a large piece of cloth used on the floor of a stage to create different effects (for example, the appearance of grass or water)

lighting rig bars from which lights are suspended to light up a stage

Your co-director has come up with the following ideas about creating the staging for the 'street' scenes.

Proposal for staging the 'street' scenes

I propose that all the street scenes take place at dusk. I think this will create an effective, moody and slightly sinister atmosphere that will go well with Jan and Mark's monosyllabic and sometimes mysterious and confusing dialogue. We can create the dusk effect with purplish lighting and use a soft yellowy spotlight on Jan and Mark, to suggest that they are standing under a streetlight. The street scenes will all take place at the same time of day, so that when we switch to these scenes the lighting will be familiar to the audience and they will know that a Jan/Mark scene is coming up. I'd also like a quiet background road noise for these scenes, and to project an image of an empty street of large houses and nice gardens on the cyclorama. This should remind the audience that this story could happen anywhere. The bench should be onstage for the street scenes, but positioned slightly differently for each – a subtle suggestion that each one takes place in a slightly different place. The actors could use the bench differently each time too. For example, in the first scene, Jan and Mark could stand facing each other at either end of the bench, but by the final street scene, they could be sitting on the bench, next to each other, holding hands. This will suggest a growing closeness between Jan and Mark, which will add an extra layer of meaning for the audience.

Activity 5

Your job is to write a similar proposal for the 'field' and 'wood' scenes. Like your co-director, make sure your proposal covers sound, lighting and visuals, and explain how you think your choices will enhance the audience's experience.

a) Proposal for staging the 'field' scenes

---

b) Proposal for staging the 'wood' scenes

Casting

All of the characters in *DNA* are teenagers, which makes it ideal for school productions. It also creates a challenge for professional theatre companies who will need access to 11 actors who can convincingly play teenagers. On the other hand, casting might be made easier by Kelly's note that the names and genders of the characters in *DNA* 'are suggestions only, and can be changed to suit performers'.

Activity 6

Answer the following questions about gender in this play.

a) Imagine the play with an all-male cast.

   i. How would this affect the central (Leah–Phil) relationship?

   ii. Would you judge the character of Cathy differently if she were renamed as a boy and played by a male actor?

   iii. Would the play be less relevant to girls if it featured no female characters?

b) Imagine the play with an all-female cast.

   Would you judge the character of Brian differently if he were renamed as a girl and played by a female actor?

c) Imagine the play cross-cast, so that the gender of the actors and the gender of the parts was ignored.

   i. How would the story change if a boy played Leah's part and a girl played the role of Phil?

   ii. Would the central action (around the character of Adam) have more or less impact on you, and why?

Activity 7

Make casting notes for each character using the template provided in the example about Brian.

Director's notes for the part of Brian

Character as written: A weak character, often crying. Mistreated by several of the other characters so has very low status.

Likely impact on audience: An emotionally genuine character, the audience may well empathise with him strongly, e.g. '…I'm crying because I'm lying and I feel terrible inside.'

Costume: School uniform, but poorly worn to indicate his low status: a shabby jumper with a hole in the elbow, dirty cuffs, shirt hanging out, tie pulled into a tight knot and askew.

Suggested physical behaviour: Needs to have behaviours that go with his low status and mistreatment, e.g. could always be wiping his nose with a dirty handkerchief or his sleeve. Never really stands up straight, as if trying not to draw attention to himself.

Physical appearance: Greasy, childish haircut. Skinny. Definitely not someone with a heroic, 'leading man' look.

Voice: Often sniffing, high-pitched and childlike. Needs to contrast with more dominant characters like Phil and Cathy.

When a theatre company decides to put on a play, various activities may be organised to help the actors engage with the plot and their parts. For example, before rehearsals there may be a read-through, where the whole cast come together and simply read the script, with no 'acting out'. This will help everyone to start to understand the main events and key actions. There may also be workshops, in which everyone tries out different ways of staging, voicing and playing their parts. All of this will help the director to make decisions about interpreting the play 'from page to stage' for the audience.

Activity 8

a) Imagine you are directing the last 'street' scene involving Jan and Mark. Choose one of the following ways of presenting the scene and explain your choice.

Staging option 1

The two actors stand very close together and whisper all their lines. The actor playing Mark keeps looking around, as though he thinks they are being spied on or could be overheard.

Staging option 2

The two actors stand on opposite sides of the stage with mobile phones and perform the scene as though they are in different streets, talking on the phone.

Staging option 3

The two actors sit side by side on a bench but each has a mobile phone and they are messaging each other rather than talking. Their lines are projected for the audience on the back wall of the stage.

I would choose staging option _____ because...

----

b) Choose one other scene from the play (not one of Jan and Mark's scenes) and devise three ways it could be staged.

Staging option 1

Staging option 2

Staging option 3

Analysing performance

When you write about how the play might be performed, you need to link your analysis to Kelly's script and the sort of experience he intended the audience to have. You may see a production of the play as part of the preparation for your exam, but don't fall into the trap of writing a review instead of an analysis.

For example, read the following extract from a student answering the question:

> To what extent should an audience be shocked by a performance of *DNA*?

This student is really struggling. The arrows below show where the teacher is going to add comments to the student's work. Look at these points and then complete Activity 9 on page 76.

1.

2.

3.

4.

5.

6.

7.

In a production of DNA that I went to see, the main character Phil was actually played by a girl and even though I know Phil can be a girl's name I found it really distracting. Also they didn't really use any proper sets – just different lighting for the street, wood, etc. One thing I really disliked about the play was the plot – I thought it was really unbelievable that a group of teenagers would get away with what they did. I think someone should of got punished. One good thing was that the actor who played Cathy was a really good actor. She had a proper mean face and when she went off to kill Adam with the plastic bag it was really dramatic. I think the whole audience was in shock. Another good bit was when Danny kept going on about the teeth – it was actually really funny and I didn't think it was a play that would make me laugh because the theme is very dark and you would expect it to be shocking.

Activity 9

Match the teacher feedback to the numbered annotation points alongside the student work on page 75. The first one has been completed for you.

Teacher feedback	Numbered annotation
Avoid saying what you liked/disliked – this isn't what the question is asking.	3
Be careful – 'should of' is grammatically incorrect. Also, think more broadly about punishment. If you really feel no characters suffer punishment, does this add to or detract from the play's ability to shock?	
Interesting point but be clearer – does the humour add to or detract from the shock factor?	
It's good to comment on facial expressions, but make a link here between the author's creation of Cathy's character and the ability of the play to be shocking.	
This opening sentence is not linked to the question. Use the key words (audience, shock, performance) to make sure your answer starts in a focused way.	
Well done on this point, which is directly relevant to the question. Expand by saying in what way Kelly managed to shock, for example through action, dialogue, character.	
You've commented on the lighting with no reference to the question. How did the lighting contribute to the shock factor?	

Upgrade

As you can see, watching a performance of a play is no guarantee you'll be able to write about it well! If you don't get the opportunity to see a production, don't worry. You can look up information and images from past productions and you can use your imagination to picture what the play would be like onstage. As a reader, you can also imagine yourself as a member of the audience, and think about how you would feel if it were being enacted in front of you.

Activity 10

Now write your own answer to the question: To what extent should an audience be shocked by a performance of *DNA*?

You can use the student answer provided to see what errors to avoid, and the teacher's comments as guidance to help you do a better job. You could try starting like this:

> An audience should be shocked by witnessing a performance of *DNA* because the subject material is truly upsetting. The death of Adam is...

Progress check

Use the table below to review the skills you have developed in this chapter. For each column, start at the bottom box and work your way up towards the highest level in the top box. Tick the box to show you have achieved that level.

I can sustain a critical response to *DNA* and interpret the performance aspects convincingly ☐	I can use well-integrated textual references from *DNA* to support my interpretation ☐
I can develop a coherent response to *DNA* and explain the performance aspects clearly ☐	I can use quotations and other textual references from *DNA* to support my explanation ☐
I can make some comments on the performance aspects of *DNA* ☐	I can make references to some details from *DNA* ☐
Personal response	**Textual references**

Skills and Practice

Understanding questions

Doing your best in any exam is all about preparation. After your close reading of *DNA* and working through this book, you should be feeling confident about the sorts of things you will write about. In this section, you will get ready for different sorts of exam questions, practise writing answers and review sample responses that you can learn from.

Activity 1

Complete the table below by formulating another example question using each key question word or phrase. You will find some exam question words that crop up again and again.

Key exam question word or phrase	What do you have to do?	Example question	Your own example question
Explore	Investigate openly and write about a range of different ideas.	Explore the different styles of leadership seen in the play.	
Explain	Put forward different views, with reasons to justify them.	Explain the importance of silence in the play.	
In what ways	Present a range of ideas and explain them.	In what ways does the structure of the play impact on the audience?	
How far/To what extent	Evaluate the level or amount of something.	To what extent do the characters in the play change by the end?	
How does Kelly	Examine the techniques the author uses.	How does Kelly create tension in this extract?	

Making up your own questions and writing essay plans and whole answers is a great revision activity. Try to do this more as you get closer to the exam, setting yourself the same time limit you will have in the exam.

In the exam, avoid launching straight into writing your answer. Make sure you really understand what the question is asking. Pay attention to the key question words and remind yourself what they mean. Turning the exam question into a mini spider diagram is a good way to help you focus on what is being asked and to start planning. Here is an example.

Focus on the language, staging and dialogue the writer uses – voices and speaking styles of different characters, how bullying is enacted or reported

Investigate and write about a range of ideas – think about the different types of bullying that different characters engage in

Explore how Kelly presents attitudes to bullying

Include different points of view about this theme – bullying used to humiliate; Cathy's enjoyment of violence used to bully others; Phil's silent control of Leah

Activity 2

Using the example above as a guide, on separate paper, explore each of these possible exam questions with mini spider diagrams.

> In what ways does Kelly explore ideas about truth and lies in the play?

> To what extent do the characters in *DNA* take responsibility for their actions?

Exam techniques

Sometimes things go wrong in exams. This isn't surprising, because people are under pressure and it's easy to make mistakes. Being well prepared includes having good exam techniques. For example, you must:

- read the question at least three times
- use some of the time allowed to plan your answer – and don't cross out your plan, as you may be given credit for things you've included in it
- make sure your grammar, punctuation and spelling are the best they can be – there are some marks for them
- answer the question!

This last piece of advice sounds so obvious, and yet every year, many students go wrong by not answering the question. Make sure you read the exam instructions and the question carefully, it and as you write each paragraph of your answer keep checking that it is focused on the question.

Getting started

Activity 3

Four students are in a panic as their exams start and they are each about to make a classic mistake. Rewrite the beginning of these answers a–c for the students, using Student 1's answer as a model.

Student 1 is answering the question 'Explore the role of Leah in the play as a whole'.

> DNA is a modern, naturalistic play in which the action takes place across three anonymous outdoor settings. It was written at the beginning of the 21st century and explores ideas of power, violence, responsibility and...

Stop! You haven't got to write everything you know about *DNA* in this exam. Focus on the question.

A better start is…

> Leah is arguably the most important character in the play. She certainly has the most lines, and she is the character that the audience gets to know best, as she is very open about her thoughts and feelings.

a) Student 2 is answering the question 'How effective do you find the beginning and end of the play?'.

> In this essay I am going to write about the beginning and the end of the play and whether I think it is effective. I will consider how the beginning hooks the audience in and how the ending might leave the audience feeling as they leave the theatre.

Stop! You are wasting time and words. Never begin an essay with 'In this essay I am going to…'. Don't tell the examiner what you are going to do – just do it!

A better start is…

----

b) Student 3 is answering the question 'Write about the ways Kelly uses Jan and Mark in the play'.

Dennis Kelly, writer of DNA, is a modern playwright who was born in London in 1970. His first play was called Debris and several of his works have experimented with theatrical structure while exploring dark ideas and difficult situations for ordinary people.

Stop! Only a small amount of this contextual information is relevant, and anyway, references to context should be made as you go along as part of your analysis of the text. Make sure your first paragraph starts to actually answer the question.

A better start is…

----

c) Student 4 is answering the question 'Explain the significance of two different minor characters in the play'.

DNA is the story of a group of friends whose bullying actions lead them into criminal behaviour. Soon after the play starts, the audience learns that a boy called Adam has been horribly bullied and, according to the other characters, is dead as a result.

Stop! You are retelling the story. Use your first sentence to make a clear case for the two characters you are going to choose.

A better start is…

Writing style

In your written responses to questions about *DNA*, it is important to write in an appropriate formal, clear style. Here are some student responses that need improvement. All the students are trying to answer this question:

Explain the role of a character who you think contributes to the dramatic impact of the play.

Student A

The character of Mark and Jan pop up again and again and they sort of have the role of a greek chorus, telling the audience stuff about the action. I reckon Kelly put them in for a bit of comedy too because they talk very fast and they say funny things that normal people might say like Jan when she says 'proper dead, not living dead?'

Student B

Phil is probly one of the most important people. though he doesn't say much. He's always eating in all his scenes except at the end. and he never answers Leah. So the ordience might think hes quite annoying. But hes important when he gives loads of orders to all the others and hes the one that thinks up the plan to cover up what they done to Adam so that means he is significant. Hes quite a leader really.

Student C

The play is full of dramatic impact and it's quite hard to choose one character that brings a lot of it. For example, John Tate doesn't seem important because he isn't in it much but on the other hand he does show leadership because he was the one who was the leader before the play started – we can see this when he is talking to Lou and he says 'who made that happen'. So he was important to the group then but because it all gets 'stressful' for him another leader has to come along and the choice is between Richard and Phil.

Activity 4

a) Identify the grammar, spelling and punctuation errors these writers have made by highlighting them and making the corrections.

b) Using the table below, review the student essay extracts against the success criteria for effective writing about character.

Success criteria	Student A	Student B	Student C	My work
Correct spelling				
Appropriate formal and wide-ranging vocabulary, expression and correct grammar				
Evidence of focus on the question (e.g. comments on character and dramatic impact)				
Short quotations embedded				
Knowledge of the whole text shown by reference to a range of scenes				
Retelling the story avoided – events mentioned only briefly with much more focus on what they mean				

c) Write your own paragraph of character analysis in response to the question:

Explain the role of a character who you think contributes to the dramatic impact of the play.

----

d) When you have finished, use the final column of the table to check you have included all the desirable features.

Exam requirements

Exams vary, as do the tasks you have to do on set books. Knowing the text as well as possible is the best way to get ready for whatever challenges you will face, but you should also find out as much as you can about the way in which you are going to be tested.

Activity 5

Carry out some research to find out the answers to the questions below. You can do this by:

- asking your teachers
- studying examples of relevant exam papers or past questions
- looking at the website of the exam board that runs your exam or coursework.

a) How much time in total will you have to read the text and get ready?

----

b) In the exam, how long will you have to write your answer on *DNA*?

----

c) Will you have to answer an open essay-style question or a question based on an extract from the play?

----

d) Will you be allowed to have a copy of the text with you when you are writing?

----

e) How many marks are available for the question on *DNA* and what percentage of the total marks is this?

However you are being tested, you need to show that you have:

- an understanding of the themes and ideas of the play
- an insight into and perception of less obvious meanings
- an ability to choose relevant evidence and apt quotations to back up points
- an appreciation of Kelly's techniques and their effect on the audience
- a clear and fluent way of writing about your ideas
- good vocabulary, and accurate spelling, grammar and punctuation.

Activity 6

a) Put the items from the list on page 84 into the following table, ranking them from 'most challenging' (6) to 'least challenging' (0). Your finished list may not be the same as anyone else's because everyone has their own strengths and weaknesses.

Exam requirements	Level of challenge for me
	6
	0

b) Focus on the two things that you ranked the highest level of challenge and therefore feel least confident about. Write two action points for each. These should be things you can do before the exam to improve your confidence.

For example, if you feel that 'understanding the themes and ideas of the play' is a weakness for you, you could decide to:

i. work through the 'Themes' chapter of this book again

and

ii. make a revision card for each main theme, including an explanation in your own words and three key quotations.

Close reading skills

Remember that, whatever the question, showing off your close reading skills is your best chance of doing well. This means you need to:

- remember the main plot events and how they relate to each other
- consider how characters change and develop during the play
- pay attention to the play's structure, language and dramatic techniques, and the effects of all these
- link plot, characters and language to themes and ideas.

Activity 7

You are going to practise bringing all your reading skills and understanding together by reading the extract below and answering the following essay questions:

a) Using this extract and two other relevant moments in the play, explain how Kelly uses the character of Leah to explore the theme of social responsibility.

b) Explore how Kelly uses dialogue to create drama in this extract and elsewhere in the play.

c) 'I think Phil is pure evil.' How far do you agree with this assessment of Phil's character?

Stage one of a good exam response is to know the extract well. Answering the questions below will help you build your knowledge. Annotate your answers onto the text below.

a) Leah takes on a range of roles in this scene. Identify lines that show her:
   i. reminding Phil that Adam used to be part of the group
   ii. feeling jealous of Cathy
   iii. showing uncertainty and anxiety
   iv. being the voice of responsibility.

b) Find two lines that show:
   i. Phil's determination to save the group
   ii. Phil's control over Cathy
   iii. Phil's exploitation of Brian.

c) Find two lines that show Brian's lack of understanding about what is going on.

d) What is the dramatic significance of Phil acting out the murder of Adam by tightening his plastic bag over Brian's head?

e) What attitudes to violence are conveyed in this extract? Use evidence from the text to support your points.

LEAH: It's Adam, Phil, Adam! We used to go to his birthday parties, he used to have that cheap ice cream and we used to take the piss, remember?

PHIL: If he comes back our lives are ruined. He can't come back, Cathy.

LEAH: Oh, great, now you're talking to Cathy, like, I'm not, I'm not, because you don't like what I say and now it's Cathy, you sit there and you say nothing for years and suddenly now you chatting with Cathy.

PHIL: Cathy?

LEAH: Let's, come on, let's, it won't be that bad, it'll be, we can explain, we can talk. We can go through the whole thing and make them understand –

PHIL: *(To CATHY.)* Do you understand?

LEAH: Understand what?

CATHY: Yeah. I do.

LEAH: Oh great, now you're at it.

BRIAN comes back, giggling.

(Pointing at BRIAN.) I mean I might as well talk to him for all the sense I'm getting. Phil, we can't do this, I mean what if he comes down next week, next year, in ten years, even?

PHIL: Take Brian.

CATHY: Okay.

BRIAN: We going somewhere?

LEAH: No, no, wait, you can't, no, this is… Cathy?

PHIL: Make a game of it.

BRIAN: We gonna play a game?

PHIL: You and Cathy are going to play a game. With Adam

BRIAN: Brilliant!

CATHY: How?

LEAH: How what? What are you, will you please talk to me as if

PHIL: Brian?

BRIAN: Who?

PHIL: Come here.

BRIAN goes to PHIL.

PHIL: I'm gonna do an experiment with this plastic bag. I want you to stay still while I do this experiment.

BRIAN: I love experiments! Will there be fire?

PHIL: *(Emptying his carrier bag.)* No. No fire. Stay still.

PHIL places the bag over BRIAN 's head.

BRIAN: It's all gone dark.

He pulls the handles back around his neck and to opposite corners, making it airtight.

BRIAN is giggling inside, looking around and breathing the plastic in and out of his mouth.

Bit stuffy.

PHIL looks to CATHY. She nods.

This is great!

LEAH: Phi… Phil?

PHIL takes the bag off.

(Three, A Wood)

Planning

Using the ideas you came up with in Activity 7, and any other relevant points, complete the following flow diagram plan for question a).

a)

> Using this extract and two other relevant moments in the play, explain how Kelly uses the character of Leah to explore the theme of social responsibility.

Opening paragraph – state that Leah is the most developed character and the only one to reflect on the wider consequences of what happens to Adam – **'we're in trouble now'** *(One, A Field 2)*. Give an example of her awareness of how humans behave in groups, e.g. her thoughts about whether humans are more like chimps (aggressive/competitive) or bonobos (empathetic/kind).

⬇

Write about other examples of Leah commenting on social responsibility and how humans need each other, e.g.:

- collective blame (**'if we have done a thing [...] we did it together'** *(One, A Wood)*)
- everyone pretending to be happy for each other
- everyone **'working together'** being a sign of things being **'much better'** *(Two, A Field)*.

⬇

⬇

⬇

⬇

Conclude by summing up the ways in which Leah shows responsibility. However, she is the one that leaves the group. Does this show that she gives up on them? Arguably, in the end, none of the characters takes responsibility for others, because even Leah puts herself first.

Activity 9

Choose either question b) or c) from the questions on page 86 and create a spider diagram essay plan to show how you would respond in the exam. Aim for five main, well-developed points and a concluding paragraph.

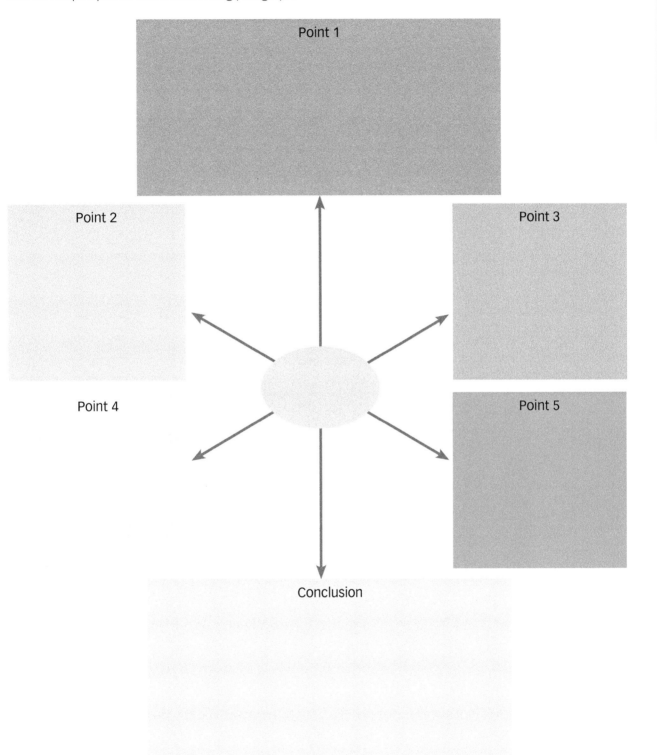

Point 1

Point 2

Point 3

Point 4

Point 5

Conclusion

Upgrade

Remember that you can use the stage directions, as well as the dialogue, as evidence to support your points about the play.

Activity 10

Read the following source text, and the example questions a) and b) that follow it. Circle the question you would answer and complete the table to show how you would answer it.

Annotate the extract and the exam question to help with your planning.

> *RICHARD enters with CATHY.*
>
> RICHARD: We just came from the police station. It's full of reporters.
>
> CATHY: It was great.
>
> RICHARD: It was shit. Phil, have you heard?
>
> LEAH: We heard.
>
> CATHY: They wanted to interview me.
>
> RICHARD: You've heard? You know?
>
> CATHY: Didn't have time, but I'm gonna go back
>
> RICHARD: So you know they've caught him?
>
> CATHY: get on the telly
>
> LEAH: How can they have caught someone who doesn't exist?
>
> RICHARD: I don't know, Leah.
>
> LEAH: Because that's impossible.
>
> RICHARD: Why don't you tell them that? Why don't you pop down the station and say 'excuse me, but that fat postman with the bad teeth doesn't actually exist, so why don't you let him go'?
>
> LEAH: Sarcasm, that's the lowest.
>
> CATHY: they might even give me money for it, do you think I should ask for money?
>
> LOU: He's gonna go to prison.
>
> LEAH: Lou, they are not going to send him to prison because he answers a description they need more than that, they need fibres, they need samples, they need evidence.
>
> RICHARD: DNA evidence.
>
> LEAH: Exactly, they need DNA –
>
> RICHARD: No, they've got DNA evidence.
>
> *Beat.*
>
> LEAH: What?
>
> RICHARD: He answers the description, but they've got DNA evidence linking him to the crime.

LEAH : DN… What are you talking about?

RICHARD: We spoke to a reporter. They matched up the DNA evidence they found on the jumper to a police database and they came up with this man, this man who answers the description perfectly.

LEAH: That's impossible.

RICHARD: Well it's what happened.

LEAH: No, because, we made that description up and they got DNA from a random –

Beat. She turns to CATHY.

Cathy?

Pause. They all stare at CATHY.

CATHY: You told us to get DNA evidence. We got DNA evidence. We did what you said.

(Two, A Wood)

a) To what extent is this a significant moment in the play?

b) Explore the ways in which the characters' interactions show different levels of power in this scene.

Opening paragraph
•
•
•

Paragraph 2	Paragraph 3	Paragraph 4	Paragraph 5
•	•	•	•
•	•	•	•
•	•	•	•

Concluding paragraph
•
•
•

Practice

Activity 11

This student chose question b). Read the following paragraph from their answer, then match the annotations alongside to the relevant text in the answer.

> Explore the ways in which the characters' interactions show different levels of power in this scene.

1. Strong analysis of language using some correct terminology.

2. Effective focus on key words in the question.

3. Strong knowledge of the whole play demonstrated.

4. Some awareness of Kelly's authorial intentions.

In this scene, it could be argued that Cathy does not have power. She hasn't yet developed the dominance that will see her take on a leadership role by the end, when she shows no restraint and is apparently willing to even 'cut a first year's finger off'. At this stage, in contrast, Kelly shows that she is sidelined by the exchange between Leah and Phil, and in her childish obsession with the possibility of TV glory and that 'they might even give me money'. Her incomplete sentences and selfish interjections underline her low status. However, the scene is a turning point for Cathy, as it is the first time that we see her take control. Seeing her take Phil's cover-up a step further than he planned, the audience get a preview of the future Cathy, who can use her 'initiative' and will later carry out Phil's instructions to the letter and commit a much more significant criminal act.

5. Embedded quotations.

6. Awareness of play as a performance.

7. Cohesive words and phrases ensure the answer flows and makes good sense.

In any exam response, make sure you use key words from the question all the way through your answer, and make sure each paragraph focuses on the question.

Activity 12

a) On separate paper, write your own practice answer to one of the questions below:

- To what extent does *DNA* communicate a clear moral message?
- Explain the importance of loyalty in the play.

b) Use the following table to check that you have included all the features of a successful answer.

Successful answers show...	Tick or cross	Example from your own practice answer for each aspect
Understanding of the themes and ideas		
Insight and perception about less obvious meanings		
Ability to choose relevant evidence and apt quotations to back up points		
Analysis of Kelly's techniques and their effect on the audience		
A clear and fluent way of writing about ideas		
Good vocabulary, accurate spelling, grammar and punctuation		

Progress check

Use the table below to review the skills you have developed in this chapter. For each column, start at the bottom box and work your way up towards the highest level in the top box. Tick the box to show you have achieved that level.

I can sustain a critical response to *DNA* and plan thorough, thoughtful and accurately written exam answers accordingly ☐	I can use well-integrated textual references from *DNA* to support my interpretation ☐	I use a wide range of vocabulary and can spell and punctuate consistently and accurately ☐
I can develop a coherent response to *DNA* and plan full exam answers accordingly ☐	I can use quotations and other textual references from *DNA* to support my explanation ☐	I use a range of vocabulary and can spell and punctuate mostly accurately ☐
I can make some comments on *DNA* and plan exam answers accordingly ☐	I can make references to some details from *DNA* ☐	I use a simple range of vocabulary and can spell and punctuate with some accuracy ☐
▲ **Personal response**	▲ **Textual references**	▲ **Technical accuracy**

Glossary

allegory a work of art that can be interpreted to reveal a hidden spiritual, moral or political meaning

catalyst something that brings about a change in the story

chorus a group that comments on the action of the play

cliffhanger a tense and exciting ending to an episode that deliberately withholds the scene's resolution from the audience, leaving them wanting more

climax the highest point of tension or most intense part of a literary work

colloquial conversational

complication when the main character's progress is complicated or reversed

context the circumstances that form the background for a piece of literature and can help readers to understand it

contraction the shortening of a word or phrase, for example, by replacing one or more letters with an apostrophe (you're, I'm)

cyclorama a cloth or screen stretched tight to form the back wall of a stage set

déjà vu a feeling of having already experienced the present situation

device a technique intended to produce a particular effect or fulfil a purpose in a literary work

dialogue speech between characters

duologue speech between two characters

ellipsis omission of words that are nevertheless able to be understood due to context *or* the three dots used to show when a character's sentence trails off

ensemble a group of musicians, actors or dancers who perform together

epiphany a moment when someone suddenly sees or understands something in a new or clearer way

expletives swearing

exposition key information about setting, characters and situations, often delivered at an early stage in a literary work

external structure the way a literary work is divided into sections

filler words empty words (such as 'like', 'you know', 'just') that carry no meaning but are often used in normal conversation

floor cloth a large piece of cloth used on the floor of a stage to create different effects (for example, the appearance of grass or water)

foreshadow to warn by mentioning in advance

hesitation a slight pause

Human Genome Project an international project to chart the entire genetic material – including all the DNA building blocks – of a human being, completed in 2003

internal structure the way a story is organised to develop the narrative

interruptions characters breaking off from their own chain of thought or interrupting others' speech to pursue another idea

jeopardy danger of loss, harm or failure

juxtaposition placing two opposite ideas or meanings near to or next to each other, to draw attention to the similarities or contrasts between them

lighting rig bars from which lights are suspended to light up a stage

monologue a long speech given by a single actor with no interruptions from other characters

monosyllabic made up of words of single syllables

monosyllables single syllables

naturalistic created to mirror real life

non-verbal communication communication without words

offstage not on the stage and so not visible to the audience

plot the main events of a play, novel, film or similar work, presented by the writer as an interrelated sequence

polysyllabic made up of more than one syllable

props moveable objects used onstage by the actors

protagonist the main character in a work of fiction

reiteration saying something again, usually to make the point clearer or for emphasis

repetition repeated words, phrases, ideas and structures

resolution the ending of a narrative where questions are answered and matters are concluded; also known as the denouement

sentence fragments incomplete sentences

stage directions indications from the playwright about how scenes should be presented or words should be spoken

stream of consciousness a style of writing that mirrors a character's continuous, unedited thoughts

subplot a secondary story told alongside or as part of the main drama

theme a subject or idea that is repeated or developed in a literary work

OXFORD
UNIVERSITY PRESS

Great Clarendon Street, Oxford, OX2 6DP, United Kingdom

Oxford University Press is a department of the University of Oxford.
It furthers the University's objective of excellence in research,
scholarship, and education by publishing worldwide. Oxford is a
registered trade mark of Oxford University Press in the UK and in
certain other countries

British Library Cataloguing in Publication Data
Data available

ISBN 978-0-19-843747-5

10 9 8 7 6 5 4 3 2 1

Printed in Great Britain by CPI Group (UK) Ltd., Croydon CR0 4YY

Acknowledgements
We are grateful for permission to reprint from the following
copyright material:

Dennis Kelly: Extracts from *DNA* by Dennis Kelly (Oberon, 2008),
copyright © Dennis Kelly 2008, used by permission of Oberon
Books Ltd.

The publisher and author would like to thank the following for
permission to use photographs and other copyright material:

Cover: © Enigma/Alamy Stock Photo; **p19**: ktsdesign/Shutterstock.